Sexual Reproduction

Susan Michelmore was graduated from the University of London with an Honors degree in Zoology and, as a student, worked at the Marine Biological Association's laboratories in Plymouth, England. Now the mother of four children, she worked for Tavistock Publications before her marriage.

SEXUAL REPRODUCTION

Susan Michelmore

AMERICAN MUSEUM SCIENCE BOOKS

Published for
The American Museum of Natural History

The Natural History Press
GARDEN CITY, NEW YORK

Sexual Reproduction was originally published in England by Eyre & Spottiswoode (Publishers) Ltd. in 1964 under the title *Sex*. The American Museum Science Books edition is published by arrangement with Eyre & Spottiswoode (Publishers) Ltd.

Sexual Reproduction is also available in a Natural History Press hardcover edition.

Contents

LIST OF ILLUSTRATIONS

Sexual Reproduction

1

What Is Reproduction?

Sooner or later nowadays most people get the chance to see a newborn baby. For nine months the fertilized egg has been growing and becoming increasingly complex inside the mother's uterus. Once fertilization has taken place the mother has virtually no control over how the baby develops. She cannot choose the sex or the color of its eyes. In fact many of the vital stages of growth go on before a woman can even be sure she is pregnant. Although a full pregnancy is forty weeks, the embryo is recognizably human by six weeks, even though at this stage it is only one quarter of an inch long. The head and heart are already formed and there are rudimentary limbs, not to mention gill pouches and a tail, perhaps making it look more like a fish than a man. It is in these early weeks that development can be upset by the mother taking such drugs as thalidomide, or in some cases by contracting a virus disease such as German measles. By eighteen weeks, when movements begin, the heart can be heard and the embryo already has such details as finger nails, eyebrows and eyelashes and external genital organs.

But where is the beginning of the story? Certainly not with the new baby. Many animals have completed their reproduction when the new young emerge, others have still to rear them; but in either case the young are the end product. Neither is the egg the start of the process. Very simple animals leave a great deal to chance when providing a new generation. For them, little happens before the release of their sex cells. For others, reproduction is a very complex chain of events, one following the other in a set pattern. These events may be described as taking place on two levels—one inside the cell itself, the other involving the whole animal. The processes going on inside the cell are naturally far less known to the average man; they are still being investigated by research scientists and they are basically the same in both the simplest and most complicated animal. These procedures determine how an egg develops, what sex the individual will be, and what characters it will inherit from either parent. The activities which involve the animal as a whole are familiar to everyone, to a greater or lesser extent. Courting, fighting, mating and the actual birth of the offspring are all readily observable and form a vital part of most animals' reproductive behavior.

The egg might seem a convenient point at which to take up the story of reproduction. Few people ever see a human egg, or have any idea of how it grows from microscopic beginnings into that complicated, red-faced, squawking object, a day-old human. In fact there are literally hundreds of different kinds of eggs in the animal world. Eggs with shells, horny eggs, shell-less eggs, vast eggs, minute eggs—all different, all fulfilling the same vital function, that of helping to perpetuate the species. Perhaps the best known is that of the hen, which immediately gives one a false impression of an egg's structure. The majority of the contents of a hen's egg, 99% in fact, is stored food; only 1% is the living cells that will grow into a chicken. It seems strange that there should be so many different sorts of egg if they are all ultimately achieving the same object. Over and over again it becomes apparent that in reproduction, as in other things, there are many satisfactory ways of solving the same problem.

While it has been obvious to man for centuries that both a male and female were necessary for breeding, the reason for this has only been known a hundred years or less. A Dutchman called Leeuwenhoek first discovered spermatozoa in 1677 and nearly two hundred years later Van Beneden and Hertwig first grasped the idea of the part played by sperms and eggs in fertilization. To understand the early development of a fertilized egg it is essential to know what that egg contains and what basic chemical processes go on in every living cell.

The word "living" is a significant one. It is freely used in everyday speech but it is very hard to define. The dividing line between a minute speck of living tissue and an inanimate chemical molecule is very fine. One of the features of being alive has been the ability of an object to make more of itself by the rearrangement of existing material and incorporation of new substances from its surroundings. A crystal in a saturated solution will grow, but this is because crystals form from the solution, the crystal itself taking no active part. Penrose has already devised a number of mechanical experiments with plywood objects that illustrate many of the fundamental processes of reproduction. He has shown that under certain conditions if plywood objects are supplied with "food" they can rearrange it to build more like themselves. It all depends on the arrangement of the component units. If these units are carefully designed, to prevent incorrect ordering, they can be made to form self-copying chains. Some device like a track ensures that they fit together correctly in relation to one another, and this can be compared to the behavior of molecules during crystallization. The objects are made to move by tilting and are shaken continuously, these processes corresponding to the various forms of energy found in a chemical reaction, dependent on light, heat and other factors.

When these experiments are repeated with the materials found in living cells, and this is not yet possible, it will be hard to say whether or not these artificial preparations are alive. Such progress depends on understanding more about the copying processes that go on in the cell. All living matter is built up of many different types of chemicals made up of molecules. The multiplication of these molecules is called replication. This procedure of making new identical molecules is the basic process in both growth and reproduction.

The chemistry of these processes, which form the foundations of life itself, is just beginning to be discovered. Living matter is divided into units or cells and these cells contain a vitally important structure, the cell nucleus. The nucleus was once thought of as a small patch of tissue in the cell with no very special structure or function. It is now known to be the vital center that controls the cell's activities.

All life starts with a single cell at some stage of its history and one of the essentials of reproduction is the copying process that enables one cell to produce another like itself. The simplest form of reproduction, when a one-celled animal or plant divides in two, is governed by a very complex series of events that ensure each half of the parent cell has identical contents. If this were not so, half might produce a daughter cell with no means of taking in food while the other half might be able to feed but not to get rid of waste matter. On a larger scale there must be a mechanism which ensures that a rabbit produces another rabbit and a man another man; anything else would be disastrous. All complex animals grow, not by the individual cells getting larger but by the number of cells increasing from one to millions. Here again the copying must be faithful if this process is to be successful.

Only the outlines of the process are at present known, but although the work may seem somewhat obscure and hard to follow, it is absolutely fundamental. It ensures that pigs don't fly or fish walk, and it is also the guide telling cells when to multiply and when to stop. When this mechanism fails and they multiply more than usual, the resultant collection of cells may form a malignant growth, or cancer.

All living things reproduce in one way or another, but what

is sexual reproduction? Since the term can be applied equally to sea anemones and men, it cannot just imply the mating of males and females, as in humans. The important thing about sexual reproduction is that the new individual is formed from the sex cells, or gametes, of two individuals, rather than being a copy of one individual. If a man could reproduce without sexual methods, he would produce one or more individuals who were exact copies of himself. The idea has a nightmare quality; there are very few people, if any, one could bear to see duplicated indefinitely. The nearest man ever comes to this is the production of identical twins, and even they seem to retain the ability to develop a certain amount of individuality. People who know them really well can usually tell them apart, and anyway they are different from their parents and their children will be different from them. In every case a child is a combination of characters inherited from the mother and father. There are so many possible variations and combinations that no two children are ever exactly alike. Anyone who belongs to, or has met, a really large family knows how great the variation can be. This variation is found in the offspring of all animals and plants who reproduce by sexual means. The vast majority of living things multiply sexually at some stage in their life history and there must therefore be some vital significance in this method. Just why it is so important will be discussed in a later chapter, but briefly it is because it allows a considerable degree of variation to appear in the character of the offspring produced. As an absurd example, suppose man reproduced without sex, and conditions were such that only people over six feet tall and under 140 pounds in weight could live in a certain place. They could have children exactly like themselves and the population would all be over six feet tall and very thin. Now suppose that conditions changed, and only short fat people could survive. Unless one person, by chance, had a short fat child the population would be unable to adjust itself to the new conditions and would die out. If these imaginary people were reproducing sexually they would be producing varying types all the time, and the community as a whole would adapt itself on the basis of the survival of the fittest. Thus variability is the key to the importance of sexual reproduction.

As animals have become more complicated, their sex behavior has also required a more delicately balanced and adjusted mechanism. The simplest animals live in the sea, and have always lived in the sea, only later conquering fresh water and land. These simple animals release their sex cells into the surrounding water, usually in vast numbers, and leave their future to chance. Some eggs will be fertilized and eventually reach maturity, but that is no concern of the parents. There may be some way in which neighboring animals respond to changes around them which ensure that the sex cells of a group of animals are liberated at the same time, increasing their chances of fertilization, but no other specialization is found. As animals became more complicated, they began to live on land and had to find new ways of breeding in these new surroundings. Fertilization became internal and animals developed means of recognizing potential mates, or persuading them to co-operate in breeding and finally in caring for the young. A tendency also developed for the males to fight rivals and to pursue the females, that they might begin courting. So in the higher animals there are complex ceremonies and patterns of activity, employing all the senses, and with the sole purpose of facilitating or effecting fertilization. This accounts for the brilliant color of the male bullfinch, for the fighting of tom cats and the changes in feminine fashion. They are all part and parcel of the sexual behavior of the animals concerned, expressed in different ways.

The sexual behavior of man is the best-known factor in reproduction and one of great interest because of its personal implications. It will be discussed more fully later, but briefly it is useful to compare it with that of other animals. There are a lot of similarities between human sexual behavior and that of a variety of animals. The lengths to which men and women go to attract a sexual partner are paralleled by the courting of birds and fish, as well as other mammals more nearly related to man. Foreplay, as a preliminary to copulation, is found in the preening of birds and the mutual grooming of apes, as well as in various forms in human sex life; but there are two basic differences. Firstly, in man, sexual behavior and reproductive behavior are no longer synonymous, as they are with all other animals. Secondly the sexual behavior of man seems to be controlled to a far greater degree by areas of the brain and to a lesser extent by hormones, circulating in the blood stream. In humans sexuality is far more influenced by learning and experience than is possible in animals with a simple brain. There is therefore a wide divergence of sexual behavior among different groups and societies of humans, "normal" behavior being dictated as much by the cultural customs of the society as by the individuals' instinctive reactions.

2

Human and Animal Societies

The idea of animal societies is a familiar one and children's quizzes and general knowledge tests often include requests for lists of collective nouns; a pride of lions, a flock of sheep, a gaggle of geese. Man, in common with a wide variety of other animals, is a social being. Social life demands one essential basic reaction, simply that individuals should be attracted to one another. This may show itself simply as swarming in response to some direct chemical stimulus, or may be a much more complicated business involving stimulation by an image presented by another member of the species. The reproductive swarming of many simple marine animals falls into the first category, while the second includes the complex processes that go on when humans are attracted to each other. True social relationships are only possible among the higher animals, where the central nervous system and sense organs are well developed. Tinbergen has suggested that social forms may be broadly classified under one of two main headings. First there are those forms where the group develops through what he calls differentiation, the individuals of the group all having a blood relationship. This is seen in its most extreme form in the social systems of insects where all the members of the community have a common mother. The second type of group is made up of animals which have no blood relationship but which become integrated to form a society. An example of this kind of community is provided by the breeding colonies of gulls or penguins, both of which gather in large numbers, as well as by men generally.

Humans are quite definitely social animals. There are a great number of different types of human society throughout the world, but the solitary human is remarkable for its rarity. The hermit, the shipwrecked mariner, the prisoner in solitary confinement, all excite the imagination because they are outside the normal compass of human experience. Recently a Frenchman spent a considerable time underground and quite alone. The sense of isolation and timelessness proved to be the greatest hardship he had to face.

The human baby is quite helpless when born, even after a long gestation period of forty weeks, when it develops in the mother's uterus. Moreover it is unable either to walk or talk, two attributes which have enabled man to master his environment. Babies utterly depend on learning these skills, particularly talking and communicating generally. It is essential for them to live in a group of individuals from whom they can learn by imitation. A child brought up in isolation, by a deaf mute, would be unable to speak or understand speech. Similarly a child can learn any of the many human languages with equal ease when starting to talk, since it is by experience, not heredity, that it learns to communicate with others. From the very earliest days development in a group is essential to normal mental growth.

In most human societies true equality between the sexes is rare. The different social position of men and women is based on their different roles in reproduction. Women bear and suckle the children; they tend therefore to be tied to the home. The men, free from such ties, hunt for food, work to support the family, or become warriors. This is a simplified picture and untrue for a number of different peoples. There are many parts of the world where the women produce the food and raise the children, taking the infants into the fields strapped to their backs. Generally speaking the male takes the dominant role and this extends to being the dominant partner in sexual relations. Men tend to be physically larger and stronger than women and are therefore able to dominate them physically. Also they are sexually active all their adult life, while women have a sexual cycle, in common with apes and other primates. The combination of male dominance and continuous sexual activity makes for continuity in sexual partnerships. This tendency is one of the basic factors in the formation of most human societies. Marriage recognizes these partnerships, and helps both to stabilize them and to ensure male help and protection to the women and children. Our own society is unusual in placing a high religious significance on marriage which more usually is a legal and social institution.

In some human societies the dominant role played by the man in the sexual relationship is recognized to such an extent that any show of emotion by the woman is considered unseemly or at any rate unnecessary. This is now a somewhat outmoded tradition in America and Northern Europe, but is still very much the case among some Eurasian and South American tribes. The Latin peoples and those of New Guinea, on the other hand, would consider such reserve unnatural and attribute it to some deficiency in the woman's character or physique. All cross-cultural references to man's sexual behavior make it increasingly clear that it is extremely hard to establish what is meant by the term "normal." Similar types of behavior may have developed independently in different, widely separated parts of the world. Frequently behavior considered normal in one society is considered a perversion elsewhere. One can only judge the normality of any individual in the context of the society of which he is a member.

A number of animals other than man show the same sort of male dominance in reproduction. Many male animals become increasingly aggressive just before actually copulating.

This seems to serve a definite biological purpose, stimulating the female, and in some cases it is the necessary stimulation for ovulation itself. Fighting, to guard the territory, and mating are often very closely linked. Whenever an animal of the same species ventures into a male's territory it will be attacked irrespective of its sex. The passive reaction of an intruding female leads the defending male on to courtship and mating, his former aggressiveness forgotten. Such behavior is true of fence lizards, where the males fight fiercely in the breeding season, the females being quite passive. Male shrews, bats and rabbits all inflict bites on their mates when mounting and mink go even further. The male mink sinks his teeth into the female's neck just before intromission and an apparently violent battle ensues. This seems to be essential before the female will ovulate and peaceful matings are nearly always sterile.

Anthropologists have shown that there are human societies dominated by women, but they are rare and not truly comparable to other, male-dominated societies. For one thing the social domination of the women does not usually extend to normal sex relationships, where the parts played by the man and woman are no different from those in any other society. Secondly, while the women may be the dominant figures in the marriage and family life, the society as a whole is still run by men. In primitive societies the social importance of the man is always increased because of the importance of his physical strength to the well-being of the group as a whole. In the Iroquois people a woman is the titular head of the family. Land passes from mother to daughter and the women are responsible for agriculture generally. They are therefore of great economic importance to the society. Even so they are dominated by their own male relatives and men handle the general tribal affairs.

Human societies are based on the partnerships formed between unrelated men and women, which can for convenience be called mateships. As with other animals, these liaisons fall into different categories, and nearly all social systems have a strict code by which some forms of mateships are recognized and approved, while others are not. These partnerships can be permanent or impermanent. The former fall into four groups, depending on the number of people involved.

Group mating—that is, where men and women of a group all mate at random—is rare and generally only occurs within a family; two or more men mating with two or more women. At one time such an arrangement was thought to be the logical transition from primitive promiscuity to a more limited type of mating. It seems to have very few, if any, advantages over other forms of marriage and to be in direct conflict with man's natural instinct to acquire exclusive possession of one or more females. It is very occasionally practiced by some members of primitive tribes in Brazil, but even then only among a very small percentage of their numbers.

Other permanent mateships can be between one man and one woman, which is called monogamy, one man and several women, which is polygyny, or several men and one woman, which is polyandry. This last type is nearly as rare as group marriage and is of little importance in most societies. It is still found in some Indian tribes and among Polynesians. In the latter, until recently, the number of females in the population was kept down by infanticide and the sharing of a woman among men acclaimed as a great virtue. It also used to be the custom among the poverty-stricken lower classes in Tibet. Here the people depended on agriculture for their livelihood but family holdings tended to be pitifully small. To minimize the demands on these scraps of land they were inherited by all the sons of the family, at least one son being expected to join a religious order and thus further reduce the claimants to the land. The group of brothers would then take one wife between them and work for her and her children. In spite of the practice of female infanticide, the woman's social stand-

ing was high and she controlled the family purse strings and
organized the menfolk. The richer Tibetans were either
monogamous or had several wives, and the polyandry was the
direct result of severe economic hardship.

Monogamy is the generally accepted practice throughout
the Western world. Multiple mateships and both premarital
and extramarital relationships are generally forbidden, either
by the state or church or both, and are considered socially
unacceptable. This is rare, however, among other human societies and although monogamy is found the world over, the
majority of other peoples recognize a man's right to several
wives, or concubines, if he can afford to support them.

Polygyny is accepted by a large number of the world's
societies. Its forms vary; a man may have one wife and several concubines, or several wives of differing social status. In
some cases the extra wives must be the sisters of the original
wife, but whatever the tribe or people, the permitted sphere
for wife choosing is strictly limited by social custom. In a vast
number of cases, contrary perhaps to the expectations of
many Western men, the husband has little say in the choice
of the second and subsequent wives. In Madagascar and a
number of African tribes the system is as follows. A man
chooses his first wife, then his free choice in matters begins
to decrease. He can take a second wife only with the approval
of the first, and subsequent wives must give their unanimous
approval before another can be added to their number. It
gets increasingly difficult to obtain unanimity, and in spite of
his apparent dominance the man is often badly outnumbered
by his womenfolk. Chiefs are the only exception. In fact
such a husband is often far worse off than his counterpart in
a monogamous society. Economic factors also limit the number of wives a man can support and, among the Eskimos and
non-Christian civilizations in India, Islam and China, only
one man in twenty is able to afford two or more wives, the
majority being monogamous.

Impermanent sexual partnerships are formed in all societies, whether or not they are socially permitted. Sometimes social codes are so restrictive that even permitted liaisons are unlikely, but this is unusual. License seems to be granted more generally to men, both mated and unmated. Kinsey, in his report on American sexual behavior, estimated that approximately fifty per cent of all American husbands had at least one extramarital experience, while among the Toda of India there is no such word as adultery. There are also communities where "wife lending" and "wife exchange" are recognized forms of hospitality. A man visiting a distant community will be "lent" his host's wife on the strict understanding that he will himself provide similar hospitality when it is his turn to play host.

The range of human partnerships is wide, but all cultures seem to be unanimous in forbidding primary incest. This is the result of social influences, not biological ones, since brother-sister matings and those between parents and offspring are common throughout the animal world, without any very apparent detriment to the species, unless carried to excess.

It is worth while, at this point, to compare human societies and mateships with those found in others. The apes, which come nearest to man in the animal kingdom, also show different types of societies. Wild chimpanzees live in groups, the males often ruling several females and their offspring. Gorillas live in smaller groups with one dominant male in control, having four or five wives and several young under his rule. Gibbons, on the other hand, are monogamous, living in family groups of one mated pair and their young, including adolescents up to eight years old. They form a close-knit unit and have a well-defined territory which they take care to keep. The other extreme is found with the howling monkeys, who live in clans. The males lead in turn and the females are common property. They all defend the common territory fiercely.

Many animals form breeding communities which break up when they have served their purpose. In most cases the male protects the females, who will mate with other males should the opportunity offer. The harems of seals are a striking example of these temporary communities. The bull fur seals arrive at the breeding grounds several weeks before the cows and, by their aggressive behavior, establish territories along the coastal fringes of the islands where they breed. Late arrivals form a second row, holding territory inland behind the first comers. Farther inland still are groups of bulls without territories and immature bulls.

Seals have a divided uterus, carrying a pup in one horn of the uterus one year and in the other the following year. The cows are pregnant when they arrive at the breeding grounds and the single pup is born within a few days, sometimes hours, after their arrival. The bulls on the shoreline get first choice of cows, and only those they miss or reject reach the second line of bulls. As soon as the pups are born the females are remated, so an adult cow seal is pregnant 99% of the year. The bulls defend their territories and their wives by roaring and occasionally by pitched battles, when they inflict ferocious bites on their opponents. The females look after the pups for three or four months, by which time they can swim and fend for themselves. By the end of the breeding season the harem masters are exhausted and completely uninterested in the young virgin females, who arrive toward the middle of August. These young females are able to mate with the young bulls who were immature at the beginning of the season and those who failed to obtain a harem. In the autumn all the animals leave the islands and return to the sea, to feed and regain their strength before the beginning of another fiercely competitive breeding season. In contrast to the fur seals, there are other seals among whom complete promiscuity is found, without either harems or territory.

Wild sheep, elk and deer also form breeding herds. F. Fraser Darling* has shown that red deer may form a number of different social groups. There are herds of hinds and young, led by an old hind, herds of stags in a much looser association, and separate reproduction groups in the rutting season. Then a stag collects a harem which is still led and guarded by a female, though he in his turn may warn her of impending danger. With both deer and elk the numbers of a harem fluctuate quite rapidly, and while a stag is fighting to maintain his harem it may be quietly divided up and driven off by other males in the vicinity.

The social communities of insects form a complete contrast to these societies. They are groups which, as mentioned at the beginning of the chapter, develop through differentiation. They are all offspring of a common mother. They mature in such a way that there are always sexual, worker and soldier individuals in the community, and there is a high degree of social organization. A termite colony may live from twelve to fifteen years. Termites, with ants and bees, live in a completely female-dominated society.

The chief advantages of these human and animal societies seems to be that they help maintain law and order. Human males, like those of other primates, are sexually active all the year round and have a tendency to accumulate and hold females. This tendency is inhibited, or curbed, by the structure of most human societies. A limit is set on the collection of females, and those collected are guarded. Thus marriage ensures that a woman and her children are under the care of a male, whose job it is to keep, protect and feed the family. Any society that fails to establish this pattern will be frequently disrupted by fights.

* A Herd of Red Deer

3

Families and Care of the Young

The human family is the unit out of which all society is built and it has always had great significance. It is more highly developed than others in the animal kingdom, and because of man's development of thought and emotions, human family bonds are stronger than those between other parents and off-spring. Even so, the importance of the family as a unit is changing and the emphasis shifting.

The European and American concept of a family is a simple one. Basically it is the reproductive unit of a married couple, their children and a fringe of relatives. This image does not apply to the families of all societies and cultures. In many places in the world the family can be described as a core of blood relatives with a fringe of spouses. In these cases when a young person marries, where he or she will live depends on local custom. In some communities the woman always goes to her husband's people; in others the reverse is true. In either case the original family ties remain even after marriage, and members of the family feel great responsibility for one another. In matriarchal societies the men that count in a boy's upbringing may not include his father, but comprise his maternal uncles. In some cases the simple biological unit of a breeding couple is completely ignored. In the Nayar tribe, in India, the man takes no place in the family as either husband or father. The woman marries a stranger and formally divorces him three days later. This man has no responsibilities toward wife or child. The women care exclusively for the children, though they take lovers, who can be dispatched with the minimum of formality. This leaves the men free of emotional and economic ties and is said to make them better warriors and mercenaries, which are the main male occupations.

In our own society it is recognized as a distinct disadvantage to be brought up without a father; many cultures try to avoid this state of affairs by forming initiation groups which are responsible for some of the education and upbringing of all adolescent boys.

There is one tendency in present-day thinking in favor of group upbringing of children. In some countries women are encouraged to return to work as soon as possible after childbirth, leaving their children to be reared in groups in state nurseries. It will take time to show whether or not these children are at a disadvantage through growing up with no home life.

The drawback of the biological family unit, as we know it, is its impermanence. If the center of the family is the married couple; then if one or other dies or leaves home, the whole family structure is threatened. In the families based on blood relationship the system has greater stability, and the loss or addition of one member makes no great difference to the family as a whole.

It is not always easy to remember, when thinking of other animals, that they do not have the same emotions as man. A blackbird deserting a nest of eggs is very different from a woman abandoning her baby on a doorstep. Both may be motivated by fear, but there the comparison ends. In fact few animals have a maternal instinct, since the vast majority have insufficiently developed brains to respond to complicated stimuli from their young. The majority show the simplest form of parental care. They make provision for the next generation by laying their eggs in a favorable place or providing large quantities of yolk granules for food, and then forget the whole matter.

These animals have no family life. Are there any advantages in a family's developing together? It does, of course, mean that the burden of rearing the young can be shared, and in man it allows the maximum use to be made of the male's capabilities. Not all male animals play a full part in community life, and the honeybee has become a byword for idleness, the drone having no use except to mate the queen bee. He serves no other purpose and is usually dead long before his young emerge from their brood cells. Since the majority of drones fail even in this one task, they seem to have scanty justification for their existence.

The longer the young animals have to grow up in a family, the further they are likely to develop. A species that is fully developed in three weeks is unlikely to reach the same level as a species that takes three years. Elephants, among the most intelligent of animals, stay together as a family for several years and the unmated females help to care for the young. Animals either started to have a family life because their young had a protracted infancy, or the new generation matured more slowly and fully because they were growing up protected by the family group.

The advantages of not having a family are more readily apparent. The patterns of behavior which link parents and children are very complex, and need not be learned by animals with no family. Reproduction is at its simplest when only one animal is involved. When co-operation between two partners is necessary, the whole process becomes infinitely more complicated. The co-operation in a family group is more complex still, and a relationship between parent and child necessitates the development of certain new instincts and the suppression of many normal everyday reactions. For instance, many young animals provide their parents with the stimuli normally connected with eating, while the parents provide the young with many stimuli normally given by an enemy. It is vital that the parents "learn" not to eat their young, and that the young "learn" to distinguish their parents from other adults. It is also important that individuals do not respond to the young and parents of other species, and that the parents defend their offspring against enemies and predators. On occasion these parental reactions fail and the family is destroyed. If a tame doe rabbit is disturbed shortly after the birth of her litter, she will kill and eat the lot, fear overriding her maternal instincts. Sometimes the young are very similar to the parents' normal food and then they must learn to distinguish their own young. Cichlid fish protect their young in a curious way. After hatching, the female fish stops feeding, and carries the young round in her mouth, where they continue to grow. Sticklebacks, another group which care for their young, seem to manage without altering their feeding habits, since the male stickleback will gather the young in his mouth if they wander too far from the nest, still foraging for food the rest of the time. Lorenz describes a delightful instance of learning in a male cichlid. This fish was collecting its young in the evening, picking them up in his mouth and returning them to the nest. On one of these journeys the adult fish saw a small worm. He hesitated, spat out the young, ate the worm and, having swallowed it, picked up the young fish and resumed his journey. These cichlids seem to learn not to eat their own offspring when they raise their first brood. A pair of cichlids, breeding for the first time, had their own eggs removed and replaced with those of another species. The pair raised these substitute young in the ordinary way, but when they kept their own eggs from subsequent matings they ate the young as soon as they hatched. An animal without a family has no need to learn these complex patterns of behavior, which are obviously far beyond the learning powers of simple animals.

In animals that care for their families, is there any connec-

tion between the size of the family and the amount of attention the parents give their young? There are people who say
they have only one child because that is all they can care
for; it is arguable whether the sort of advantages given to the
child are the ones that will best fit it for adult life. In animals other than man, the offspring of small families get more
attention and care than those of large families. This is for
several good reasons. If infancy is prolonged, and this presupposes that the family bond is strong, there will be a limit to
the number of young that can be reared in any given period
of time. This problem can be posed in quite another way. If
an animal produces only a few young, it is essential that a
high percentage reach maturity and breed themselves if the
species is to continue and flourish. An animal that produces
vast numbers of eggs can afford to lose a few during development. There is no sentiment in the animal kingdom; the only
important thing is to maintain the species, replacing the wastage of old and injured individuals with new ones. An eagle,
who has few enemies, produces only two eggs in a clutch;
while a songbird, less able to protect itself and its young,
lays an average of four to six eggs.

Young animals emerge into the world in every stage of
maturity from utter helplessness to complete independence.
Are there any advantages in producing helpless young? Birds
and mammals are the only two groups to produce offspring
who are completely unable to fend for themselves. In mammals the most helpless babies are generally born after a very
short gestation period. This could be taken to mean that
some animals are better suited to caring for their offspring
after birth than to having a long pregnancy. It means that a
mouse can have a great many litters in a year, since she can
become pregnant while still suckling the preceding litter. The
longer the young take to develop in the uterus the fewer can
be produced in a breeding season. The problem with birds
is somewhat different. The world of the developing bird

embryo is bounded by the egg shell, and there is a limit to the amount of food this can contain. By hatching in a helpless state, young birds can take longer to develop and can finish growing in the nest, fed and cared for by their parents. Hens are able to include far more food in their eggs than a blackbird, and chicks emerge very well developed compared with the scrawny, naked blackbird nestlings.

So much for the advantages of producing helpless young. What are the advantages of well-developed offspring? For some animals this is essential. If a young antelope were as helpless and unco-ordinated as a human baby at birth, it would soon die. It is vital that the mother and young of all free-ranging animals should be able to keep up with the herd, and young zebras, giraffes and horses, to name but a few, can all run quite fast a few hours after birth. This is their only hope of avoiding their natural enemies. Nearly all invertebrates produce eggs which they never see again. These must hatch as self-supporting individuals or die. They are generally produced in large numbers to allow for the inevitably high percentage of mortality during development. The parent animals have neither the brain nor central nervous system to care for the developing eggs and young.

This means that family life is limited to a few groups of animals, but there are all sorts of animals who instinctively make provision for their offspring without realizing what they are doing. In the simplest form, the eggs are laid only where they will have a good chance of developing, while in the most complicated form, provision is made by animals who build nests. Birds are the first group of animals to come to mind in connection with nest building. They certainly make the most elaborate nests of any animal and may go to enormous lengths to camouflage the nest and insulate it, to protect the nestlings and help keep them warm. At the beginning of the breeding season birds start to go through a chain of actions, of which nest building is one. There are numerous ceremonies associated with the nest and nest building which give it a greater significance than it would have if it were simply the place where the eggs were incubated. Birds that build more elaborate nests seem to recognize the nest itself rather than the eggs inside. This probably explains why a cuckoo can lay its eggs undetected in the nest of another bird. Herring gulls and geese, on the other hand, which only build rather crude nests, recognize their own eggs, and if an egg is stolen by another bird the enraged parent will claim it and roll it back to the original nest site.

The style and site of the nest follow a definite pattern for every species of bird. An oyster catcher will always nest on the ground, a woodpecker will always choose a hole in a tree. Some birds seem to have great latitude when choosing nesting sites, and robins may select one of a wide variety of places, ranging from a mossy bank to the hood of a car or a discarded saucepan. Tits will use nesting boxes providing they are suitably sited and allow room for brooding after the eggs are laid. None of the actions connected with nest building are consciously directed towards the welfare of the next generation. The bird experiences a series of impulses that automatically lead it from one stage to the next—courting, mating, nest building, egg laying, brooding and so on. It is merely responding instinctively to the various stimuli which are only present at this stage in its life cycle.

One fascinating speculation is how this sort of thing started. At some time some bird must have built the first nest, just as millions of years ago a man built the first crude house. The process has become elaborated gradually through the years. In other places different animals have found a similar solution to their breeding problems. South America is the home of several species of frog. In these tropical regions conditions are ideal for growth, and developing young need neither warmth nor insulation. What is needed, however, is a sheltered place where a young frog can develop quickly and safely, and this is provided in a number of ingenious ways. One species makes pockets from folded leaves, cementing the edges together to make a little bag, which holds enough water for the developing eggs. Another collects beeswax, forming it into cement. This cement is then used to line a hole in a tree, making it waterproof and providing a little pool where the eggs can hatch. Even frogs that live on the ground make nests. They dredge mud from shallow ponds and form it into little rings above water level. Whan it rains these fill with water, forming artificial lakes where the frogs lay their eggs.

These frogs are unlike the majority of nest builders in that they take no further interest in their young. This abandoning of the young is found in other animals that take great trouble to hide their eggs. Turtles go to elaborate lengths to hide their eggs in the sand, but their interest then ends. Similarly a number of insects use their bodies as drills to make hiding places for their eggs, yet they never see their offspring.

Egg-laying habits would not seem so queer if they happened at random. It is the regular pattern of events that seems a little uncanny. The haphazard nesting habits of the robin sometimes cause surprise, but they seem more explicable from the human viewpoint than those of an animal that will lay its eggs only in one particular place. The bitterling, for example, is a small and not particularly distinguished fish. It is noteworthy because it always lays its eggs inside the shell of a clam. How the eggs avoid being swept into the clam's feeding current and eaten is a mystery. What is more, the female bitterling has had to develop a long egg-laying tube to get the eggs into the shell in the first place. How did the first bitterling come to lay eggs in a clam? Once the habit was established it had advantages, because the clam provides shelter and the eggs are kept aerated by the feeding currents. The same sort of thing is found with the lacewing fly. This fly lays its eggs on slender stalks on the branch of a tree. The eggs wave about like ears of corn above the bark, and when they hatch, the larvae fall down onto the branch, ignoring the other unhatched eggs above them. If a stalk is accidentally bent or broken, the larvae immediately eat the egg. If the eggs were laid directly on the bark it is probable that only the first one to hatch would survive. How did the first lacewing come to lay its eggs on stalks?

More remarkable than all these developments are the animals that migrate vast distances to reach suitable breeding grounds. Here the urge is sustained for long periods of time, and is so strong that the animals can overcome seemingly impossible conditions. The story of the eel has long been a zoological classic but at present some zoologists doubt its authenticity. The salmon is, however, known to journey great distances and to make the change from salt to fresh water in the bargain. Adult salmon live in the sea, but at the beginning of the breeding season they make their way up the great rivers of Europe and the North American continent. They forge on and, where they encounter obstacles, will leap again and again until either they are successful or their strength is exhausted. They spawn near the sources of the rivers. Some die, but many make the return journey, followed later in the season by the young fish who finish their growth in the sea. When these are ready to breed they will follow their ancestors' routes, apparently tending to return to the rivers where they themselves were spawned.

Birds and butterflies also migrate to their breeding grounds. One migrant familiar to everyone goes a step further. The arrival of the cuckoo is timed to coincide with the beginning of the small songbirds' breeding season, because it is their nests which are used. The adult cuckoo is not a parasite, but its young are raised by other birds at the expense of their own brood. This is the cuckoo's way of providing for the next generation. It lays its eggs in the nests of such birds as the hedge sparrow and robin. When the young cuckoo hatches it has an insatiable appetite, opening its beak wide and gaping for food. The foster parents respond to the cuckoo's gape by filling its beak with food. Since it is larger and more distinctive when gaping than the other nestlings, it is fed at their expense. It finally heaves them out of the nest and they lie unnoticed on the ground, dying of cold and starvation.

This is also a good illustration of the lack of "maternal instinct" in birds, in the sense in which we apply the term to man. A hedge sparrow expends a great deal of time and energy feeding its young and one would be justified, on these grounds, in describing it as a devoted parent. It is quite unreasoning, however. As long as there is a gaping beak in the nest it will do its best to fill it. It is incapable of distinguishing the intruder from its own young; in fact the parents are more strongly stimulated by the vigorous cuckoo nestling and their own young go unheeded.

The cuckoo is unusual in "farming out" its young, but several insects have equally ingenious ways for feeding their offspring. Ichneumon flies lay their eggs in diseased maple or elm trees. These trees have already been attacked by the horntail, an insect whose Latin name is Tremex, whose larvae bore galleries in the wood. The female ichneumon fly walks over the tree, "sounding" it until she is over one of these galleries. She then bores into it with her ovipositor, laying her eggs in the horntail's tunnels. When the ichneumon eggs hatch, the larvae feed on the horntails. The female ichneumon fly needs very highly developed sense organs to be able to detect the diseased trees and find a suitable spot to lay her eggs. Other insects, while not going to these lengths, lay their eggs on material that will serve as food when the larvae emerge. The blow fly lays its eggs on decaying meat, and the cabbage white butterfly chooses young cabbage plants.

All these animals are without further parental responsibility. Having made instinctive provision for the next generation, they either feed, to prepare for the following breeding season, or die. Their eggs are generally produced in large quantities to allow for wastage, and they have no communal family life. In spite of the advantages of such a system, a wide range of animals either incubate eggs or bear their young alive and continue to feed and care for them during their infancy. Some brood their eggs, others defend them, not always a simple task. The female octopus broods and guards her eggs, not to keep them warm but to make sure they are aerated and are not eaten by the male. She continues these duties until the eggs hatch. This may be from fifty days to four and a half months, depending on the water temperatures.

Temperature presents problems to all cold-blooded animals; the difficulty is to raise the temperature sufficiently to hatch the eggs. Pythons brood their eggs and by shuddering movements generate a little warmth. A stout lizard, called a skink, goes off when brooding and basks in the hot sun; when suitably hot it returns and warms the eggs. Crocodiles do not brood their eggs, they bury them in the sand. They do stay near at hand, however, and when they hear sounds of the young crocodiles hatching they break up the mud over the eggs and help them to climb out of the egg shells. Mother and young stay together for about twelve months or until she finds another mate.

The classic examples of incubators are birds; that this is an instinctive action can be shown by removing the eggs and hard-boiling them. If the eggs are replaced in the nest the bird will brood them all summer. One bird which normally has a hard job, without brooding hard-boiled eggs, is the male ostrich. He sits on up to one hundred eggs at a time, the eggs being laid by the wives in his harem. Having laid their eggs, the females leave the hapless male to brood them in a communal nest. A more attentive mother is the female earwig. It is hard to imagine an insect such as an earwig with much family life, but the female's care is essential to the welfare of the young. Earwigs pair in September and the couples live together throughout the winter in small chambers excavated in the soil, or under the shelter of a stone. The female lays her eggs in February and then either she drives the male away or he deserts her. She stays with her eggs, occasionally taking them in her mouth and licking them. This licking is vital if the eggs are to hatch successfully. If all goes well the eggs hatch at the end of March and the little earwigs remain under the shelter of their mother's body until they are about two months old. Very little is known about their diet during this time except that they eat their cast off skins when they molt.

Another unprepossessing insect that makes elaborate preparations for its young is the dung beetle. These largish beetles are found on open sandy land in the south of England, and the male and female work closely together in the breeding season, preparing a place for their young. In the early spring the female starts to sink a deep shaft in the ground, while the smaller male carries the soil away to the surface on his broad back. Later the male collects pellets of rabbit dung and drops them to the female at the bottom of the shaft. When she has finished digging the shaft she excavates small chambers, which act as nurseries. She kneads the dung into sausages about three inches long and half an inch thick and puts one in each nursery chamber. Finally she lays an egg in the soil near the end of each nursery, and when the grubs hatch they feed on the "dung sausage." The sinking of the shaft takes three to four weeks, and each chamber an additional ten days, so the beetles show remarkable perseverance in completing such a task. The work is finished in May or June when the parents separate. It is thought that the male only lives one season and soon dies, but that the female stays near the shaft and looks after the young while they develop.

All types of parents are found among insects. Sometimes

the female does no more than lay her eggs on a plant that will supply food when they hatch; others, like the dung beetle, go further and provide food that will be available at hatching. Hunter wasps stock larders with small insects which are not dead but merely paralyzed and are "fresh" when young wasps need food. The most specialized care for their offspring is shown by social insects such as bees, ants and termites. The cell in which the egg is laid and the type of food provided determine the young insects' future position in the colony. In a beehive the developing grubs are fed on honey regurgitated by the workers, and the eggs laid in the larger "queen cells" are fed on a diet rich in protein. These eggs grow into fertile females who are the potential founders of new communities.

Worker bees prepare food especially to feed the grubs. This is a more advanced form of maternal care than simply leaving the young with a supply of food. Some seed-eating birds go so far as to change their own eating habits in the breeding season so that they can give the nestlings suitably soft food, such as caterpillars and soft-bodied insects. Many fish-eating birds partially digest the food and then regurgitate it to feed their chicks. The young thrust their beaks down their parents' throats to get the semiliquid feed. Hummingbirds make a mixture of nectar and partially digested insects and place it into the beak of their minute nestlings. Very few animals feed their offspring on secretions, the great exception being the mammals, who produce milk from their special mammary glands. The mother needs a combination of instinct and learning to feed her young; she has the instinct to suckle but must learn to recognize her own child. A sheep recognizes her lamb by its smell; a cow seal knows her calf's voice; a human mother has to learn by sight and sound.

Animals which make special secretions to feed their young are not common. Are many raised by the male alone? In humans it is usual to think of the maternal instinct as an integral part of every woman, but this is far from the case. Just as there are some hens that will never hatch a satisfactory clutch of eggs, so there are women who have no interest in children or raising a family. In the penguin rookeries of the Antarctic the females make a crude nest, lay their eggs and then go off to the fishing grounds, leaving the male alone to brood the eggs. The females stay at sea, feeding and playing throughout the whole incubation period, but they do return to the rookery when the egg is due to hatch and help to raise the chick.

The female sea catfish does not even make this contribution to the upbringing of her offspring. She lays between fifty and sixty marble-sized eggs and then swims off. The male then performs a remarkable feat. His mouth is only about four fifths of an inch across, yet he gathers up all the eggs in his mouth and carries them for two months until they hatch. He goes without food all this time, and aerates the eggs by letting a stream of water enter his mouth and go out through his gills. Even when the eggs hatch into little fish, about two inches long, the male's job is not finished. They remain in his mouth, feeding on the remains of their yolk sacs. Only when all the yolk has gone and they are about four inches long do they finally leave the male's mouth.

Not all the males that look after their young go to such lengths. The male stickleback guards the eggs and young fish and the male sea horse carries his eggs round in a pouch on his stomach. He even invites the female to place her eggs there, displaying his empty pouch. The male water bug is not so enthusiastic. The female cements the eggs onto his back and he seems to spend much of his time trying to rub them off. The male mid-wife toad is another that seems to be trapped into looking after the eggs. The string of eggs gets tangled round his hind legs while he clasps the female during mating, and they stay twisted round him until they hatch.

It is more usual for the male to take little or no part in

family life. This is less true of animals that have a protracted infancy, when both parents are often equally involved in the tasks of feeding and teaching their young. This long learning period is an important factor in man's development and is one of the reasons he has been able to advance beyond other animals.

4

Courtship

Up to this point reproduction has been considered from a rather general standpoint. Basically it is a process that concerns two individuals, or sometimes only a single animal. When two individuals are involved, the problem arises of how they shall find one another at precisely the right time and place for mating. A large number of female animals are ready to mate only at certain times, when their eggs are ripe. It is essential for the male to be on hand, or the moment will be lost. What is more it must be the right kind of male. The animal world would be a very Rube Goldberg affair if any adult male could mate with any female, irrespective of kind or species. The many kinds of behavior that serve to bring sexually mature adults of any one species together for mating are all covered by the term "courting."

Why is courtship necessary? It is by no means universal. Sea anemones do not court one another; neither do starfish. This is true of many of the animals that live in the sea or fresh water. They have no courtship or mating procedure, simply discharging their sex cells into the surrounding water when they are mature. This obviously simplifies life, but even these animals need some mechanism to make sure that ova and sperm are released about the same time. Most gametes can live for only a comparatively short time after being set free, and both must be present and alive for fertilization to take place. If the sexes are separate, the animals must attract one another about the time that their sex cells are ripening. If the process of fertilization takes place in the female's body, there are further problems. When the males and females of any species congregate or pair during the breeding season, the female is often unprepared or unwilling for mating to take place. She must be wooed and won over by the male's courtship, so he can place his sperm in her genital tract.

Courtship has one other vital function. It prevents animals of closely related species from interbreeding. This is because courtship and mating are really part of a chain of events, one leading to another until the eggs and sperm are released and fertilization takes place. The chain will be completed only if each of a number of stimuli is received by the animals concerned. One false step and the chain is broken. No two species, however closely related, have identical courting patterns and they therefore fail to provide the appropriate steps in the chain that leads to mating, when courting an animal from a different species.

The idea of the species was brought into prominence by Charles Darwin. It is not some mystical scientific concept. In fact naturalists exploring virgin forest in Brazil found the natives' grouping of the trees corresponded almost exactly to their biological species. In other words they fell into the groups naturally. People who have never heard the word "species" realize that the lion and tiger come from different animal groups while the Negroes and Chinese are part of one diverse group. In Darwin's time the study of species was hampered by lack of both information and equipment. Since those days the development of genetics has thrown more light on the subject. It now seems that these groups are separated from one another by various means which collectively are called "reproductive isolating mechanisms." This sounds complicated but in fact simply means there are factors which act to prevent random breeding between different species; one of the most important of these is courtship.

Once it is accepted that courtship helps species to keep their identity, the intricacy of some rituals becomes easier to explain. The more related species there are living in an area, the greater is the importance of any means of preventing interbreeding. In these circumstances the development of complicated rituals is also accompanied by an elaboration of some of the animal's body structures that help to differentiate between closely related species.

If populations adapted to different ways of life interbred freely, they would undo much of the work achieved by natural selection. The specialized populations would tend to disappear and be replaced by a medley of forms; widely different genes would be brought together and delicately balanced growth patterns upset. In fact, mating between species often results in hybrids that either fail to develop or develop with a severely reduced vitality. The separation of animals into different species avoids this deleterious interbreeding between populations. Courtship is a vital part of the complete process of maintaining the species intact.

The very complexity of courtship activities presupposes that the animals taking part have a highly developed nervous system and sense organs. They must have an acute sense of sight, hearing and smell or touch, or a combination of any of these. They must be able to move and respond to complicated stimuli. So it is not surprising that the most elaborate courting goes on in the vertebrates, and that other animals with well-defined mating patterns are found among insects, crustaceans and mollusks which, though primitive, often have well-developed central nervous systems. There is an interesting sidelight on courting which may be mentioned here. In those species where mating is a very transitory affair, and where hybrids might easily appear, the difference between the sexes is often particularly marked and the species are called dimorphic. It is common in many birds, such as the cock and hen pheasant, or even the everyday blackbird.

It is easier to understand the importance of the part played by courtship in keeping the species distinct when considering a definite example. There are two species of stickleback, one with three spines and one with ten. They are closely related and may live at close quarters with one another. Their courtship rituals are very similar but there is one vital and distinctive difference. The three-spined sticklebacks are a brilliant red during the mating season, while the ten-spined variety are black. The fish will follow each other's courtship dances so far and no farther. When the courtship has started there is a sudden break in the process if the prospective mate is the wrong color, and the courtship peters out. A three-spined stickleback cannot get the right responses from a black ten-spined fish and vice versa. So interbreeding is prevented. The birds of paradise of New Guinea are famous for their magnificent plumage and exotic dances. These characters have probably developed as isolating mechanisms preventing the many closely related species from interbreeding.

Courtship has three main functions. It helps prospective mates to recognize one another, it may help in the actual choice of a partner and, thirdly, may serve to persuade the female, who is generally initially reluctant, to mate.

Recognition is obviously particularly important. If one can't recognize a likely mate the whole mating process comes to a dead halt. During the mating season the male is apt to be aggressive, most of the fighting being linked with the acquisition and defense of territory. If the female is to mate she must subdue the male's aggressiveness, or she herself will be attacked. Sometimes the shoe is on the other foot. The female is very belligerent and the male must distract her attention, or mollify her, if he is to mate with her and escape with his life. Male robins are very aggressive and when one invades the territory of another, the owner will attack the invader and drive him off. There is no difference at first glance between a male and female robin. But when a female arrives in a male's territory her behavior is sufficiently different to appease the male, and he will start displaying, preening and strutting. Similarly the American fence lizard, Sceloporus, is very aggressive in the mating season, and the male defends his territory fiercely. In the early spring the sexes tend to ignore each other and lie basking in the sun. Later, when they begin to establish ill-defined territories, the males start to attack one another. The males are distinctive in that they have a brilliant blue stripe down each side. But if a stripe is painted on the female's side, she too will be attacked by a male if she enters his territory. Similarly, if the male has his stripe covered he may be courted as a female. Here color and pattern are as vital as movement in the recognition of a male.

Courtship not only enables like-minded animals to recognize one another in the mating season, but it also helps to appease aggressive partners. When one of a pair is inclined to be fierce or predacious, his or her mate often collects gifts and presents them as a distraction, rather like giving a difficult child a toy while trying to cram a spoonful of food in its mouth.

Sometimes these gifts not only mollify, but also serve to arouse some form of parental instinct. These ceremonies are often connected with food and are ritualized as courtship feeding. Many gulls beg for food from their mates as a normal and necessary prelude to copulation. The behavior of courting robins is enough to prove that food begging has nothing to do with hunger. A female robin will entreat a male for food, while herself standing in the middle of a laden bird table. There are times when this courtship feeding is an urgent necessity. Flies of the family Empidae can mate only if the male gives the female some food. He therefore secretes a bubble of silky material in the middle of which is embedded a small insect. He gives this present to the female who starts to devour it. As long as the food holds out and she is occupied with eating it, she allows the male to mount her and mate.

As soon as she has finished sucking the juices from the gift, she discards the silk bubble and her mate with one movement. Other closely related flies do not always bother to include food in the "gift parcel." They may put in a tiny stick or leaf or even use the discarded bubble from another fly. This still serves its purpose, distracting the female's attention and allowing mating to take place. One species is more friendly; the offering contains food regurgitated by the male and is shared by male and female alike.

These male flies are merely rejected if their gift is insufficient or unsuitable in some way. The male praying mantis has to face greater hazards. The female of this species is particularly ferocious and during courtship the male approaches her warily. If she moves forward he disappears in fright. If she remains quiet he finally gets close enough to leap on her back and mate. If he lands fair and square, all is well. If he misses, he is unlikely to get another chance. The female seizes his head and starts to eat him; he may even be eaten while his hind end completes the mating. This does not seem an ideal form of courtship feeding.

The third purpose of courtship besides recognition and appeasement may be selection of a mate. This is sexual selection, and may involve the definite choice of one particular male by a female or may be just male combat.

In some of the cases where the female exercises a choice, she seems to be as influenced by the territory the male occupies as by the male himself. Humans are not unique when they marry for money. Many of the small male perching birds, such as are commonly found in fields and gardens in this country, fail to breed because they fail to establish a territory. The females seem to exercise some degree of choice in that they do not mate with the first unmated male they meet.

Territory is important to fish as well as birds. The sunfish is an American pond fish with an enormous mouth. In the breed-

ing season the males all clear a piece of ground for themselves and then lie waiting for the arrival of a female. If another male enters this cleared ground the owner adopts a
very threatening attitude, raising his gill covers and opening
his huge mouth. If the invader persists he will be attacked.
The female is distinguished by her swimming action, and as
soon as one enters a male's territory he becomes excited and
starts to follow her around. If she is sufficiently stimulated she
will stay and mate, or she may go off in search of other males
and new territories and the process is repeated.

There are cases where the female not only makes a definite choice, but where this seems to result in the more fertile
males being chosen. The ubiquitous fruit fly, Drosophila
melanogaster, provides an example of this. Working with
these flies, Maynard-Smith bred virgin females both with outbred males and with those of an inbred strain. When the
outbred males were used, 90% of the females were mated
within an hour, while the inbred males achieved mating in
only about half the cases. The females with outbred males
laid over a thousand eggs, and while those mated with inbred
males laid the same number, only about a quarter hatched.
This was due to the fact that the inbred males not only produced fewer sperm, but what they did produce was inade-
quate in some way. Maynard-Smith was also able to show that
when given the choice the females chose outbred males in
preference to the inbred ones. This comes about in the following way. When a male first notices a female he approaches
her, circling round so as to face her, head to head. If the
female does not turn away she begins a very rapid side-stepping dance when approached by the male, and he also side-
steps so as to remain facing her. Finally she stands still, per-
mitting the male to mount and mate. The pattern of courtship
is the same whether the male in question is inbred or outbred.
The inbred male often fails to keep up with the female in the
side-stepping dance, and when he falls behind he is rejected

and mating does not take place. Here the male with lesser physical capabilities is also the male with lesser fertility. Although these experiments were made with laboratory populations of highly inbred males, it seems probable that the same sort of thing happens in the wild. The female has a greater chance of exercising a choice when the males of a species are polygamous, but it will only benefit her if the male she chooses is more fertile.

Why is it that the vast majority of display is done by male animals? The females play a subsidiary role even when they exercise a final choice. The situation with man seems rather contrary to the general pattern of courtship. This was even truer in Victorian times than it is today. Then the initial display was by women, who had to make themselves sufficiently attractive, in a very discreet fashion, to induce the men to start paying them court. What purpose does the debutante season in today's society serve if it is not to display the charms of the young women to the eligible males? There are few examples outside the human species where the female plays the dominant part, but they do crop up from time to time. For instance, there is a handsome and conspicuous bird which lives in the tidal marshes in the south of the United States and is called the boat-tailed grackle. These birds have blue-black and purple plumage, shot with green, and the populations contain twice as many males as females. The males gather in parties on the ground, or in low bushes. Occasionally they make short, excited flights, but most of the time they stand rigidly, beaks up and tails depressed, like china black-birds holding up imaginary piecrusts. From time to time a female will join one of these bachelor parties and immediately the males get excited and start displaying. The female flies off and all the males follow. If they fail to excite her she will outstrip them and join another party, and so it goes on until she finds a suitable mate. She edges him to the fringe of the group, separating him from the flock, and they go off and mate. The others, rejected, abandon the chase and resume their rigid postures. Soon after mating, the female abandons the male and rears the young on her own, together with other females, a few males standing guard over the whole colony.

Females who take the initiative are rare, and the males are generally more ready to mate, if not all the time then for the greater part of the breeding season. Courtship can be described as a way of passing time. The male courts the female while he is waiting for her to reach the same state of readiness as himself. Does courtship affect ovulation? The production of eggs, particularly yolky eggs, is quite a drain on the female. It is important that these eggs be fertilized and not wasted, if the species is to flourish. Obviously the best way to ensure this is for the female to delay ovulation until she is courted, since this presupposes that a male is on hand, ready and willing to mate. There are quite a number of species where ovulation is under nervous control, and in these animals courtship provides the necessary stimulus. Such animals as cats, mink, wood rats, rabbits, some squirrels and a number of birds are among those who do not ovulate regularly. Stroking the neck of a pigeon may be sufficient stimulus to make it ovulate, and a stickleback can be persuaded to lay her eggs if she is repeatedly touched with a glass rod, imitating the quivering movements of the male. Why don't more animals delay ovulation until courting begins? Presumably the wastage is not enough to justify the development of such a step, and it is not possible for animals with a simple nervous system, since their sense organs are insufficiently developed. One of the alternatives seems to be the system found in humans. Here the female ovulates regularly year in, year out, regardless of whether a male is present or not. This practice is also followed by the cuckoo, and it is significant that this bird is promiscuous and has no known courtship activities.

How often is courtship mutual? Does one or the other sex

always take a dominant part? In some species it is not only mutual, it is a social activity, and the whole colony becomes involved. In elephants and monkeys, both social animals, and in birds where both parents help to rear the young, the mutual caresses of courtship help to forge a bond between the parents, keeping them together until their offspring are able to fend for themselves. In humans, where the care of the young goes on for longer than in any other animal family, the bond between the parents lasts ideally throughout their life together. Other animals which mate for life often renew courtship in the late winter and early spring.

Egrets, those snowy white birds whose feathers were once prized by milliners, have a prolonged courtship. There is a period of about ten days after pairing when the male and female caress each other, grooming each other's feathers with their bills and snuggling up close to one another. This "honeymoon" period apparently stimulates the female to ovulate, for they mate and build a nest. Both parents help to rear the young and during this time the mutual caressing continues.

The mutual courtship of social animals may affect all the animals in the colony. If one penguin adopts an ecstatic attitude, for instance, hundreds of others may follow suit. Similarly, herring gulls are stimulated by display among their neighbors. It has also been claimed, by bird watchers, that the mating activities of greenshanks will stimulate green sandpipers, with whom they often associate along the tide line; and that in colonies of two species of penguins all began to lay on the same day. Various zoologists have spent some time studying colonial animals; the work of Darling seems to bear out the general conclusions of all. He found that large colonies of herring gulls tended to lay their eggs earlier and to have a shorter breeding season than gulls in smaller colonies. This is an advantage since it reduces the number of hazards to which the eggs and young are exposed; this means that the colony as a whole is more successful, since more chicks will reach maturity. Similarly with seals: the cows come ashore to breed and those in large colonies tend to breed earlier and to spend a larger portion of each day out of the water with their calves. This affords the calves greater protection, and more survive than in smaller colonies.

While mutual display may arouse a colony to greater sexual activity, the sight of a pair of animals mating often arouses others of the same species to extreme aggressiveness. One of the advantages of territory is that it affords animals some degree of privacy during mating. This aggressiveness is very closely related to sexual stimulation. Much of the female's part in any courtship ritual is the appeasement of aggressiveness in the male. In a species where the male and female look alike, the female is often only distinguishable by her different behavior. If, for instance, a male black-crowned night heron adopts a subservient attitude on entering another's territory, it will be treated like a female.

When the female is very aggressive, her mate often finds it politic to arrive with a small present which distracts her while they mate. At other times the male can gauge the female's readiness to mate by her treatment of his offering. Young men laden with flowers and chocolates might almost be included in this category. Animals which behave in this way were mentioned earlier. There are yet others which make use of similar ceremonies to recognize a mate. The male tern, a dapper little sea bird, catches a small fish which he holds crosswise in his beak as he parades up and down the beach. He goes on doing this until a female arrives who is prepared to accept the fish. This is the signal for the male to start displaying, and if the female is co-operative he mounts and mates. He then helps her to make a shallow depression in the sand that serves as a nest.

All gift ceremonies are fascinating, but the most spectacular are performed by the various species of bower bird. These birds are found in New Guinea and Australia, and although related to the gaudy birds of paradise, are all rather drab and dowdy in color. The male builds an extremely elaborate nest, a very rigid structure, which he then proceeds to decorate with stones, berries, leaves and flowers. He keeps the precincts of the nest spotlessly clean, removing dead leaves and foliage daily. The different species may resemble one another very closely indeed except in the color with which they decorate their nests. The satin bower bird even paints sticks, using berries and charcoal for paint. This bird may be counted among the very few genuine avian tool users. The female is led into the bower, where the male displays, surely a close parallel to the human gambit "Come up and see my etchings." It is not certain whether the birds mate in the "courting bower," but the female makes another nest in which she lays her eggs and raises her young.

On a less exotic note the male wren also builds a series of nests to attract the female; these vary, for some are bizarre, some workmanlike, some only half finished. He, like the bower bird, displays in front of them and this attracts the female. When she has accepted him and they have mated she builds a new nest, often destroying the male's handiwork in her search for suitable nesting material.

There is a slightly different twist in the ceremonies of the adele penguin. These comical birds waddle round the penguin rookeries, collecting round stones which they present to the female of their choice. If she accepts the gift it is added to the pebbly edge of her nest. Usually there is a shortage of suitable round stones, and pilfering is common. Scientists, wishing to watch this petty thieving, colored various stones in a colony in the hope of being able to watch their progress from nest to nest. They found, quite unexpectedly, that the red stones immediately appealed to the females and were stolen with the greatest regularity. A male who was able to find a red stone had the greatest chance of succeeding in his courtship.

Nearly all the forms of courtship considered so far seem to involve a high degree of visual stimulation in one or both partners. Is courting restricted to those animals with well-developed eyesight? What happens to nocturnal animals and those with poor eyesight? Does their courtship have to be very different from that of animals with good eyesight? Song duets are undoubtedly very important to nocturnal birds. This is an interesting development, because normally the female is not as good a songster as the male. It is essential she should remain undisturbed while incubating the eggs, and she has no need to advertise territory, as does her partner. So the development of female song for courtship is contrary to the general pattern of development; it could be an adaptation to leading a night life. These songs range from the glorious liquid notes of the nightingale to the harsher noises of owls and wood rails.

Fireflies use visual stimulation when courting, even though they are nocturnal animals. The males emit a series of flashes which attract the females, the pattern of flashes varying from species to species. The females must be very sensitive to the nature of the signals to be able to distinguish between them. By imitating the male with a special type of match, it has been proved that the vital factor in recognition is the time interval between the flashes and not the nature of the light.

In general, animals will tend to stimulate each other in courtship by means of whichever sense is most highly developed. In man, where there is little to choose between the sharpness of the senses, all five are employed during courting.

Animals who do not place great reliance on their eyesight often have a very highly developed sense of touch. This is very noticeable in blind people, partly compensating for their lack of vision. Some animals rely almost entirely on their sense of touch during courtship. The tarantula-like spiders of western American deserts are a case in point. At the beginning of their courtship dance, in self-defense perhaps, the male places his foremost legs over the poison cups of the female and they perform an intricate series of steps before mating takes place. The male's eyesight is so poor that should he lose contact with the female's body during this dance, they would walk alone, side by side, unaware of one another's presence, and naturally in this case would fail to mate. One wonders how they ever manage to make contact in the first place.

The lamprey, a fresh-water eel, also relies on touch to a very large extent, having degenerate eyes. In the breeding season lampreys swim up streams and rivers to mate and lay their eggs. From time to time they pause, attaching themselves to rocks by means of their jawless, suckerlike mouths. There they remain, gently swaying in the current. The males do not stay attached to any one place for long, constantly changing from stone to stone until eventually they find a second lamprey onto whom they fasten. If this lamprey is a male, he will soon loosen his hold on the stone, and they drift downstream together, soon to separate and repeat the process. If the male attaches himself to a female she retains her hold, and this enables him to identify her. Later they swim together to a sandy place where they can mate and lay their eggs.

Some animals rely on sight, some on touch, to recognize a mate. What about the sense of smell? Anyone who has kept a bitch knows how large a part smell plays in the courtship of dogs. So much so that industrial chemists have developed various deodorants which are supposed to counteract the bitch's natural odor while in heat, and enable her to be taken out with some degree of safety. Dogs rely on their sense of smell to a very great extent in all their everyday activities, so it is not surprising that courtship is no exception. Moths also attract one another by their scent glands, and the delightful tropical lizards called geckos seem to rely on a combination of touch and smell. They are gregarious nocturnal animals, somewhat clumsy and always bumping into one another. When there is a collision during the breeding season a male gecko will seize whomever he meets. If he seizes another male, the second gecko will fight to free himself and they separate after a brief struggle. If a female is seized she remains passive in the male's grasp, and mating soon follows. The process of recognition is not entirely tactile, since if their nostrils are plugged the animals show no signs of courting behavior. Obviously, therefore, they rely on their sense of smell at some stage of their courtship.

Some marine animals stimulate one another by a means similar to that of scent—namely, they let off chemicals into the surrounding water. Various species of echinoderms, the group name for starfish, sea urchins and sea cucumbers, release a chemical with their eggs which causes others of the same species to extrude their sperm and eggs. This is hardly courtship as demonstrated by birds and mammals, but it serves the same purpose. Whales also give off a chemical which helps compensate for their poor vision.

Courtship displays range from the extremely simple to the arrestingly spectacular, and the most spectacular of all are the courtship dances. All sorts of animals, from spiders to man, dance while courting their mates. Sometimes only two animals take part; sometimes the dance is a communal activity with a great deal of intricate ritual.

These dances may influence the female's choice of mate, as in the fruit fly where the outbred males were better able to dance than the inbred ones. Here agility and fertility were apparently linked. Some spiders never mate without prior courtship dancing, and when two males perform before a female spectator she will prefer the more vigorous male. This is not always the case. Many toads, lizards, frogs and salamanders dance during courtship. These dances appear to have no effect on the female's choice of mate, but they probably stimulate her and make her receptive to the male's subsequent advances.

Many of the most spectacular dances are performed by birds, and a number of these are closely paralleled by the dances of man. Sometimes this is purely imitative on man's part, at other times the dances seem to have developed along similar lines.

Anthropologists have found that one of the oldest forms of communal human dance is the ring type, which is also performed by birds such as wild turkeys and rose-colored starlings, and is even included in the courtship rituals of spiders. Another parallel between man and birds is found in the seated dances of the South Sea Islanders. They move only the upper half of their bodies and they look very like gannets when they do their solo posturing.

Chimpanzees are social animals; they form groups, taking part in a primitive round dance. They love to decorate themselves with anything that will dangle or swing, and show a distinct sense of rhythm. This is a social dance but they also perform simple dances prior to sexual contact.

In both birds and man erotic dances are often associated with aggressive displays. An erotic dance may be added at the end of a war dance, or the women taking part in war dances may become sexually aroused. Blackcock and ruffs have communal displays and, like human war dancers, they too combine a degree of aggressiveness with sexual stimulation.

Many of the dances of modern man involve a high degree of autointoxication which serves as a sexual stimulant. In the East this state may be such that it leads to a trance or a frenzy bordering on madness.

All these dances fall into one of two categories. Either they continue over a long period of time between a pair of animals, forging a bond between them, or they are a short ceremony immediately preceding copulation. Both are equally valuable in perpetuating the species.

Courtship serves a number of different purposes, and is therefore varied in the form it takes. It is a means of ensuring that a pair is ready to mate in the same place, at the same time; it helps mates to recognize each other or pacify one another; and it prevents their mating with other species. Courtship is essentially a process of sending out signals to which the other sex responds. It is a vital step in the chain of events that leads to mating, the climax of reproduction.

5

Sexual Behavior

Little has been said, as yet, of the sexual behavior of man.
Man is an animal, and there are many similarities between
various types of human behavior and that of other animals.
There are also very important differences. The patterns of
sexual behavior in the majority of animals are due to their
biological heredity. Their responses are instinctive and the
same as those of their parents and grandparents before them.
This is not the case with man. From their earliest years men
and women are taught, either directly or indirectly, about
sex. What is even more significant is that the teaching differs
from society to society. Sexual practices considered taboo by
some cultures are highly acceptable to others. The result of
this is that an adult's view of what is proper and normal in
sexual matters depends entirely on the society in which he
was reared.

As an example, consider the question of teen-age morals.
A great deal is written in the press these days about the low
standard of morals among present-day teen-agers. A large
number are known to have some sexual experience in their
early teens, and the proportion of illegitimate births has risen
since the war. By the standards of our society these things are
reprehensible and therefore condemned. It is essential for the
general well-being of the community that its standards should
be upheld and not flouted, but in this case society is partly
to blame. Considering other races in the world, the picture is
not so alarming, or inexplicable. The barriers of the Victorian

age have gone and nothing has been put in their place. Co-
education is common, and the lack of adult supervision widespread. In both English and American society there is a
double attitude to these young people, who are expected to
learn self-control with no definite lead from the adult community. Generally, in other parts of the world, societies which
are very strict in respect to premarital sex relations find it
necessary to restrict their adolescent members in other ways,
keeping them under close chaperonage after puberty or in
separate communities. It may be that in our modern society
we have removed the physical restraint on young people
without altering the moral code. Other cultures, which encourage young people to experiment in sexual matters from
their earliest years, would find this viewpoint hard to understand; while the societies that advocate the death penalty if
a couple are found having intercourse before marriage would
think us ridiculously lenient. It seems that if young people are
to be thrown together more than ever before, it is unlikely
that moral codes evolved in the days of strict chaperonage
will prove sufficient to hold them in check. In a hundred
years' time either the degree of freedom or the attitude of
the society will have changed.

The climax of most sexual behavior is copulation between
two members of opposite sexes. This they have in common
with all other animals. Unlike the majority of animals, where
the male copulates from the rear, the most common position
for human coitus is some variant of the face-to-face position;
this appears to be general for all societies and cultures. The
frequency, time and place for coitus vary both with the race
and individuals concerned. In general there is a desire for
privacy among all peoples, and mating is controlled by domestic conditions. In other words the influences are cultural,
or learned, rather than basic and instinctive as they are for
other animals.

While coitus is the climax of sexual behavior, there may be

elaborate foreplay leading up to this climax. This foreplay is quite separate and distinct from the rituals and postures of courtship, although its general purpose is much the same. Courtship is concerned with finding a responsive member of the opposite sex, with a general view to future mating. Foreplay takes place only immediately prior to actual copulation. While it seems general among mammals, in man it is dependent on his social and educational background and the tribe or society in which he lives.

In all mammals, and especially in the subhuman primates, it is usual for the male to investigate the female's genitalia, by handling or licking, just before mating. This leads to increased sexual excitement in both partners, and in some species the female may similarly stimulate the male. A female kangaroo rat, ready to mate, will lick the male's penis repeatedly until he is sufficiently aroused. The same sort of behavior has been seen between elephants just before mounting. Human couples can be found all over the world who regularly precede copulation with foreplay, but the extent to which it is practiced depends on their social and cultural background. For instance, when Kinsey investigated sexual behavior in America he found that more men with a college education favored foreplay than those with a lower standard of education. There are parts of the world where all forms of sexual stimulation, except that from actual intercourse, are considered immoral, but this is not the general attitude. The majority of mankind, who are free from these taboos, use foreplay in the same way and for the same purpose as all other mammals. It heightens the degree of arousal of both the sexes and helps to synchronize the behavior of the pair.

Man is the only animal that has to contend with a sense of right and wrong. What an individual considers right or wrong in sexual matters is conditioned by his upbringing and background and bears little relation to the impulses obeyed by other mammals.

Incidentally, before leaving the question of arousal during copulation, it is interesting to notice that while the male orgasm is an essential part of copulation, the female orgasm is not only inessential but is frequently absent. Social surveys have shown that a proportion of married women, who consider their sex life quite satisfactory, have never experienced an orgasm. The male orgasm generally occurs within a few minutes of intromission, after which there is a period of recovery when there is little or no response to renewed sexual stimulation. The female, however, is apparently stimulated for as long as contact with the male is maintained and where intercourse is prolonged, women may achieve several orgasms.

The foregoing discussion of coitus and foreplay presupposes that the pair in question are both basically ready and willing to mate. However, a great deal of human sexual behavior is designed to attract the opposite sex with a view to selecting such a partner. This is quite distinct from courtship. Courtship is concerned with persuading a chosen individual to mate. Attracting the opposite sex *en masse* is a complicated business, since man uses all five senses to evaluate a potential partner. The last half century in the Western world has seen the capitalization of all human behavior connected with sex. Advertising has used sex appeal as the cornerstone of numerous campaigns. This is possible because American society and, to a lesser extent, that of Europe place a high value on romantic love. They are unusual in trying to make romantic love the basis for marriage. Even today there are many different countries where marriage is a matter of family policy. Young people are expected to choose their marriage partners from an approved section of the community. This is based on the very sensible theory that if two people have similar backgrounds and wish to make a success of marriage, they will be able to form an agreeable partnership, ultimately developing a real fondness for one another. This may seem a prosaic form of marriage to Western eyes, but it has proved eminently workable in Eastern countries. The idea of romantic love was first introduced into Europe by the troubadours of the thirteenth century. They considered such an experience beyond the reach of a normal married couple. It was accepted that people formed violent emotional attachments to members of the opposite sex, but such people were considered to be the tragic victims of fate. The stories of such famous, and ill-starred, lovers as Romeo and Juliet and Abélard and Héloise serve to illustrate the point.

Whatever form of marriage is finally contracted, sexual attractiveness is still important. In man all the senses play a part in assessing a potential partner, but one of the most important single factors is physical appearance. The interesting thing is that the criteria by which attractiveness are judged vary widely from culture to culture. Female beauty is generally coupled with sexual attractiveness, but the features considered beautiful show a wide variation from place to place, and even from generation to generation. In general youth is more attractive than age, and a very masculine type of woman less attractive than a well-developed feminine type. A good complexion and general cleanliness seem generally admired while baldness and extreme corpulence, in either men or women, tend to lessen their sex appeal. But there the general gives way to the particular. Some races think the shape and color of the eyes all-important, others think the particular development of some body organs necessary for beauty. What is intriguing is that a woman considered outstandingly beautiful by her own people may appear repulsive to those of another race.

Man's capabilities and skills are held more important than his actual appearance. One has only to think back a couple of generations to realize how even in England fashions in attractiveness have changed. Skills once considered essential to every man have become obsolete, and a woman who was thought a peerless beauty in Edwardian times would have got scant attention in the late 1920s.

Physical appearance is not the only important feature in sexual attractiveness. In man, as with other animals, both scent and sound can also play a part. If the advertisements in many of the present-day magazines are to be believed, a woman has only to use one of a number of perfumes to become irresistible to the male sex. Whether or not this is true, many different peoples do use both scented leaves, flowers and actual perfumes to make themselves more attractive to members of the opposite sex and to mask or destroy undesirable body odors.

Finally a brief word about love magic. Nearly all societies have developed some form of love magic, and while in the Western world these customs may only linger on as superstitions and old wives' tales, they are still widely used in other places. Charms, potions or other remedies are available for people who seek the response of a particular person. These customs have become most highly developed in societies where direct invitation to future sexual activity is either prohibited or restricted by social convention. Peoples and tribes who are accustomed to ask each other outright for sexual favors have little use for such magic and mysticism.

The age at which all these types of sexual behavior become apparent varies with the individual. The attainment of full reproductive maturity in man is a very gradual procedure and may cover a period of eight or nine years. The onset of this maturation is called puberty and is obvious because of various physical changes in both girls and boys. In the former it is characterized by the beginning of menstruation and the development of the breasts; in the latter by the deepening of the voice and the growth of facial hair. There are also glandular changes which are less apparent but more important. In the early days of adolescence the ovaries and testes rarely produce fertile eggs or sperm and the uterus is not sufficiently developed to retain a fertilized egg. Maximum fertility and reproductive efficiency are reached gradually some years later. The time taken for this maturation shows wide variations between individuals, but generally speaking the majority of people, male or female, are not capable of reproduction much before fifteen years of age.

While sex play is common among the young of many animal species, human societies vary widely in their permissiveness of such practices. It seems that the "higher" an animal is in the kingdom, the more important is the part played by learning in all its activities. Some degree of learning seems to be necessary before a chimpanzee or some of the other apes can mate successfully, and this learning is acquired in the normal sex play of the young animals. It is possible that humans who grow up in very restrictive societies, where all childish sex play and premarital experience is taboo, may have a far harder job to adjust to the patterns of normal married life than an individual growing up in a freer society. It is evident that even in the most restrictive societies immature males and females engage in some forms of erotic play, and all societies tend to place fewer restrictions on boys than on girls. In any case ignorance and lack of preparation for marriage are likely to reduce greatly the chances of the couple's finding mutual satisfaction and well-balanced adjustment. It is understandable that an individual brought up to regard all forms of sexual stimulation as wrong may find the necessary total change of outlook on marriage hard to achieve immediately after the wedding ceremony.

So far the only type of sexual behavior considered has been that involving males and females. Sexual relations do however take place between members of the same sex both in humans and a number of other animals, and a wide variety of animals also practice self-stimulation.

Our own society disapproves of any form of homosexual behavior, but such an attitude is by no means universal. The fact that homosexual alliances are found in all societies and cultures, and among other animals, would seem to suggest that while this form of behavior is not normal, neither is it a perversion. In some societies all the males form both homosexual and heterosexual partnerships, bearing out the fact that human sexual behavior is controlled and directed by learning and experience. Some cultures consider a period of homosexuality essential for developing boys, who will later marry and form the usual heterosexual relationships. It seems probable that homosexual behavior is more common among adolescents than adults and among men than women. All men and women are capable of responding to a wide range of erotic stimuli. Generally the inclinations to form relationships with members of the same sex are not as strong as those leading to heterosexual relations. But all societies force modifications on the individual's genetic background and the ultimately preferred kind of behavior is influenced by experience. So men and women who are unconscious of any homosexual leanings are as much a product of conditioning as exclusive homosexuals. Both are extremes that have moved away from the normal intermediate type capable of both kinds of attachment. In a restrictive society the majority learn not to respond or even to recognize homosexual stimuli, while a minority become highly sensitive to the attractions of members of the same sex. It is the result of a common tendency, present in all mammals, modified by experience and not due to hormonal disturbances or inherited perversions.

Another basically mammalian trait, often regarded as unnatural, is masturbation, or self-stimulation. It seems to be a natural sexual activity among lower primates and probably originated among animals that cleaned their genitalia by licking. As with other sexual practices, different cultures and societies hold widely divergent views as to the desirability of such behavior, but it occurs among adults of all societies and is commoner among men than women. While many societies ignore, or even permit, such activity among children, it is generally frowned upon among adults, where the censure ranges from strict punishment to mere ridicule. Again, however, it seems to be a basic mammalian sexual tendency rather than a perversion and its low incidence is due primarily to social conditioning.

While heterosexual partnerships are the generally accepted "normal" expression of sexual behavior, other types are found throughout the mammals, and their expression or suppression in man is due more to his social environment than to his genetic constitution.

6

Mating

Mating is a vague and general term that covers the multitude of different ways in which ova and sperm are brought together, so that fertilization can take place. It is the climax of courtship and the focal point of all reproductive activities.

In man the whole situation is very different from that found in all other animals. There is no one time in the human estrus cycle when coitus is particularly likely to take place, and consequently the chances of fertilization are less than in some other animals. This term estrus cycle is used to describe the rhythmic ripening and shedding of eggs which goes on in all mammalian ovaries during their adult reproductive life. In the majority of mammals the time when the female is most willing to mate coincides with her period of maximum fertility. Human sexual relationships have highly developed social implications and form the foundations for marriage and family life in most human communities.

Man is the only animal where sexual intercourse is not solely a reproductive function but also has a profound influence on both social and cultural life. If human sexual intercourse were confined to the female's heat period, as in other animals, the pattern of society and its general structure would be very different.

Simple animals have no need of complex mating procedure, and for the vast majority of invertebrates, living in the sea and fresh water, mating is a pretty random business. In fact all their activities are as uncomplicated as possible. Food is often obtained by merely straining particles from the surrounding water, which also takes away the waste products and provides the gases in solution needed for breathing. They simply shed their eggs and sperms into the water and leave the rest to chance. Fertilization is external and the subsequent development of the fertilized egg has nothing whatsoever to do with the parental animal or animals. Occasionally there is some means of synchronizing this release of sex cells so that there is less wastage than in a completely random process. Even in these cases the animals do not develop any special physical structures for mating; a simple animal is perhaps characterized by this lack of specialization and by the fact that the body is subdivided into comparatively few different parts.

The production of eggs, however small, is always a drain on the female's reserves of strength. Even the smallest egg is provided with some stored food material for the use of the developing embryo, and this stored material is supplied by the mother. Animals tend to produce a few large eggs or a large number of small ones, and either way it is something of a strain. It is important, therefore, that the maximum number should be successfully fertilized so that they can develop further. The number fertilized will depend on three principal factors. Firstly, the number of ova and sperm liberated at any one time; secondly, their distance apart in time; and lastly how close they are. In other words, maximum fertilization will come about when all ova and sperm are set free by the very mature animals in a very limited area at the same time. The time factor is particularly important because these sex cells can only live for a very short time once they have left the parent animal's body. There are a number of ways of meeting these requirements and increasing the chances of successful fertilization. Sometimes the sex cells, or gametes, are only released when the parent is stimulated by some chemical in the surrounding water. This is the case with some kinds of oysters and some of the marine nereid worms found along the shore and in deeper water. Sometimes the factors which control spawning are very precise, and mean that all individuals within an area will be stimulated at approximately the same time; an animal whose response is so precise is the palolo worm, whose spawning is confined to a few hours in the year.

A completely different way of solving the same problem is found by animals that live in some form of group. Fish living in shoals, birds in nesting colonies, animals roaming in herds, all stimulate each other and tend to condense the length of their breeding season with great success. The ultimate refinement is the association of sexes in pairs and the development of internal fertilization.

There are animals in all stages between these two extremes of random external fertilization and true internal fertilization, with its development of complicated associated sex organs and special behavioral patterns. These gradations are plainest among animals living in the sea. The animals that simply release their eggs and sperm into the sea have already been discussed and include many types of animals ranging from the jelly fish to the sea urchins. Some animals have developed refinements which make the whole business slightly less haphazard; ripe sea urchins set free a chemical in the water that causes other sea urchins in the area to lay their eggs or release sperm. By and large it is an extremely uncomplicated and inefficient way of mating, the eggs and sperm being at the mercy of wind and tide, not to mention hungry fish.

The first step forward is made by animals such as lobsters which adapt a pair of legs to ensure that the sperm reaches the female's storage organs, so that they are on hand when she is ready to lay her eggs. Next come the fish who have true internal fertilization, without any special mating organs. They mate by apposing their genital openings, the sperm passing straight from male to female; the openings often become swollen and rigid because they contain blood vessels which dilate as the time for mating approaches. Although there are no special structures to help these animals to mate, they need to respond to one another's signals very accurately to make sure they are ready at the same instant. Finally there are the animals like the whales which have the complete set of structures necessary for mating on land. They are, after all, mammals and their immediate ancestors were not marine but land animals. The male whale has a well-developed penis, and he uses this to place sperm in the female's genital opening, just as do related land animals.

There is then a sort of scale between animals where mating is extremely random and where it is extraordinarily precise. Closely associated with the form of mating is the size of the egg produced by the female. One of the characteristics of the eggs shed at random is that they include only a small quantity of yolk, and the animals are therefore able to produce them in very large numbers. It would obviously be disastrous to produce one immense yolky egg and then abandon it, with a small chance of its ever becoming fertilized. Sometimes the quantities of eggs released are really prodigious. The American brine shrimp, Atremia, lives in the salt ponds and alkaline lakes of the United States. These shrimp lay their eggs in such quantities that they form an encrustation all round the edges of these lakes and remain there for some months until the salinity of the lakes falls with the coming of the spring rains. While in their dry condition they are occasionally picked up on the feet of passing birds and carried to new lakes and ponds, a way of overcoming the problems of distribution. The eggs themselves are less than a sixty-fourth of an inch in diameter, and yet these belts of dry eggs may measure as much as fifteen feet and be two or three inches deep. These are not the only water animals to lay vast quantities of eggs. A female cod may lay six million in one breeding season, a salmon thirty million, and it has been claimed that a sea hare, a distant relation of the garden slug, has laid four hundred and seventy-eight million eggs in a few weeks. The idea of assessing such a total is overpowering. Humans and other highly specialized mammals are unique in laying a very few minute eggs, but because of their peculiar method of development they can contain only one or two at any one time before birth, and the developing embryo has no need for large quantities of stored yolk.

The animals that have evolved some way toward internal fertilization tend to show a reduction in the number of eggs they produce. Some animals in this sort of "halfway house" are the sea anemones. A sea anemone cut in half longitudinally has a body plan similar to an old-fashioned inkwell. The eggs are discharged into the center of the inkwell, whose scientific name is the central coeliac cavity. The sperms of other anemones are chemically attracted into this cavity via the mouth, with a current of water, and there fertilization takes place. The embryo starts to develop inside the parent and later is either expelled or swims off under its own power. It then settles and develops into an adult sea anemone. Clams have a very similar pattern of development. In a clam the folds of the gills by which they breathe lie parallel to the muscular foot of the animal, and when the eggs are laid they are lodged in these gill folds, water is drawn through the gills, and the animal uses this water current both to obtain feeding matter and dissolved gases for respiration. During the breeding season sperms are also drawn in on this current. They somehow manage to evade the film of mucus, which acts like a conveyor belt and traps particles of food and carries them to the mouth. The sperms pass through minute holes, or pores, in the gills and fertilize the eggs lying in the folds. As with the embryo sea anemone, the clam embryo begins to develop in the parent's gill folds before being expelled into the outside world. The tapeworm differs from head to tail, the head segments having male organs and the tail piece containing ripe fertilized eggs. The method of fertilization is very similar to that of the clam and the sea anemone. The mature sperms are set free into the gut of the host animal and they swim down the alimentary canal till they reach a mature female segment; in fact they are probably carried down by the natural contractions of the gut, rather than by their own efforts. Fertilization takes place in the female segment, and the segments full of fertilized eggs eventually break off from the parent animal and are passed out of the host's body. Their further development is generally arrested until they are swallowed by another host animal, when they start to grow in the normal way.

When the male places sperm in the female's reproductive tract, some form of courtship is essential. This is so for a variety of reasons. Generally speaking, it is only possible if the female is co-operative, and courtship provides the necessary nervous stimulation. Secondly, she must be maneuvered into a position where she can not only receive the sperm but retain it. The problem is obviously different for land animals. Internal fertilization became essential, since sperm can survive only in a solution of some kind, and this was problematical. Both sea and fresh water provide an aerated medium in which the sperm could swim freely and fertilize the eggs. The sperm of land animals had to be provided with a similar medium by one of the parent animals. These secretions may also supply the sperms with nourishment on their journey up the female reproductive tract.

Fertilization is not the only problem for a land animal; the embryo also needs a safe place in which it can develop. Sometimes this is provided by the mother's body, sometimes in other ways. Birds, for example, have internal fertilization; the eggs and sperm fuse high up in the oviducts. This means that there is still time for the fertilized egg to receive the protection of egg and shell membranes before it leaves the female's reproductive tract. These membranes allow the young bird to develop in a wide range of places, safe in its own little world inside the egg shell. Man and other mammals have internal fertilization and then provide food and protection for the developing embryo in the mother's uterus. The majority of birds and fishes with internal fertilization still have no specialized structures to help them mate, though they may have very complicated behavior patterns to synchronize their mating. They simply place their genital apertures close together when ready to transfer sperm to the female.

Other animals do not leave this delicate operation so much to chance, and within the animal kingdom there is a wide diversity of organs used for copulation. These range from only slightly modified general body structures to such highly specialized organs as the mammalian penis. These organs are often developed in conjunction with set patterns of behavior and such mechanisms as the mammalian estrous cycle. Each ovulation is preceded by a "heat" period when the female shows greatest sexual desire, and, in the most highly specialized, ovulation is delayed until after copulation has taken place.

Coitus, with the development of the penis and associated structures, is such a focal point in human sexual relationships that it is easy to forget that it is only one of the very many ways animals have devised of mating. The problem of transferring sperm from the male to the female has been solved in a number of different ways. The sperms may be liberated in a fluid suspension, even in animals who have special organs for placing them in the female; or they may be packaged in some way. Sometimes they are surrounded in a thick layer of mucus, or jelly; sometimes they are enclosed in a spermatophore, which is a more solid container. All these methods demand some form of courtship to ensure that the female is receptive, but it does not always follow that the actual process of fertilization takes place when both male and female are there.

The mole crabs of the Atlantic coast of the United States have a courtship ritual which serves to show the males which females' eggs are nearly ripe. It also induces the female to stay still enough for the male to deposit his sperms. Yet the male is no longer there when the eggs are actually laid. Male mole crabs are much smaller than the females and their fourth pair of legs are specially adapted for holding onto her. If a ripe female mole crab buries herself in the sand, the male will burrow in close to her and wait for her to emerge, clinging closely when he can. During courtship the female remains still long enough for her partner to wind a sperm-laden ribbon onto her underside. He then drops off. When she lays the eggs they are fertilized by coming into contact with the sperm ribbons although the male is by then far away. She tends the eggs alone until they hatch, some four or five months later.

Lobsters are closely related to mole crabs and yet their mating procedure is entirely different. The sperms are not formed into ribbons but are in a more fluid medium. During mating they are transferred to special receptacles in the female's body and there they are stored until she is ready to lay her eggs. This is no easy matter, for these animals are clumsy and the process demands very precise manipulation. The male has to get the female to lie on her back, then he holds her walking legs and pincers motionless with his own large claws. The end of the female's abdomen is cupped with his tail. His first pair of swimmerets, one of the abdominal appendages, are modified to form a duct along which the sperm and mucus can pass. These small modified swimmerets are found at the front of the animal's abdomen and they are placed in the female's receptacles with the help of the male's fifth pair of walking legs. Then, like the male mole crab, having placed the sperm the male lobster goes away.

The female rights herself and waits until she is ready to lay her eggs. Then, rolling on her back once more, she thoroughly cleans her abdomen and swimmerets. Thus prepared she lays her eggs, discharging sperm from the receptacles at the same time and churning the two together with her swimmerets. She carries the eggs about for ten to eleven months, driving a current of water through them by the movements of her legs. During this time she is said to be "in berry."

These shelled animals have complicated ways of mating but they are not so bizarre as some of the worms. There is a sea worm, called Platynereis megalops, which forms swarms at spawning time. When a large swarm of males and females has gathered, the females proceed to bite off the males' tail segments, which contain the mature spermatozoa. Luckily for the males, all nereid worms have well-developed powers of regeneration, and they swim away to grow new segments. In the meantime the cannibalistic female has swallowed the tail segments and the sperms are liberated by the action of her digestive juices. They penetrate the wall of the gut, finding their way into the body cavity, and locate and fertilize the ripe eggs. The female's body then ruptures and the eggs escape into the sea. One of the interesting features of this peculiar way of mating lies in the fact that so far zoologists have failed to fertilize this worm's eggs artificially in sea water. For some unknown reason the passage of the sperm down the female's digestive tract is essential to successful fertilization.

This method of "absorbing" the sperm, rather than placing them directly in some part of the female's reproductive system, is not confined to sea worms. Some animals whose sperm is enclosed in little packets, or spermatophores, seem to place them at random in the female's body. For instance the leech, which is an unattractive animal, has similarly unromantic mating habits. The male's sperms are contained in spermatophores which he cements onto some part of the female's back.

These spermatophores seem to contain some irritant substance which causes an ulcer to form underneath them on the female's skin. The sperms are drawn into the female's body through this ulceration and while the skin heals the sperms travel to the ovaries, where they fertilize the ripe eggs. There is a strange animal called Peripatus, intermediate in many respects between the segmented worms and the insects, who mates in a similar fashion. Some forms of Peripatus attach a spermatophore to the female's back just as the leech does. Again an ulcer forms and the sperms enter the female's body cavity, making for the ovaries. They appear to have an additional function to the sperms of leeches, in that the first sperms seem to activate the ovary, causing ovulation and fertilization to take place only if sperms from another spermatophore arrive. Other varieties of Peripatus have improved on this method of mating, avoiding the risk of infection through the ulcers caused by the spermatophores; nonetheless it still sounds unpleasant. The male's reproductive duct ends in a sharp spine which he drives right through the female's skin, placing the sperms directly in her body cavity. This method of injecting sperm into the female seems to have also developed independently in the bed bug and some kinds of flatworm.

In most cases it is easier to give a female a spermatophore than it is to introduce a suspension of sperm into her body. The latter operation generally needs some specialized organs used only for this one purpose. There are animals, however, who manage without a lot of complicated secondary sexual organs; one of these is the earthworm. Since they are hermaphrodite they do not have to worry about finding a suitable partner of the opposite sex; any other mature earthworm will do as a mate. This does not mean they have no problems. Since they have neither arms, legs, nor any special mating organs they have to solve the question of how to remain close together while exchanging spermatozoa. They achieve this by coming to lie head to tail, with the undersurfaces in close contact. They then each secrete a mucous sheath in which they become enveloped. There is a particularly close adhesion between the saddle or clitellum of one worm and the ninth

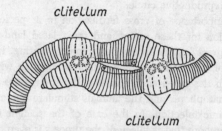

[1] *Earthworms, which are hermaphroditic animals, in copulation. After Grove.*

and tenth segments of the other, which bear the openings of the sperm receptacles. They achieve this adhesion partly by the action of the clitellum itself and partly by driving their chaetae or bristles into one another. The sperms come from the opening of the male ducts of the fifteenth segment along a groove on the underside of the worm to the clitellum and so into the sperm receptacles of the other worm. This means that during mating sperm is passing in opposite directions along the groove of the two worms. Later they separate and secrete a cocoon which contains both ova and sperm, and they finally cast off the cocoon with a series of jerks.

This mutual exchange of sperm in hermaphrodite animals seems to have been developed almost to absurdity in the sea hare, Tethys. This animal is found in quite large numbers along the Pacific coast of the United States, and in spite of its name is in fact a type of large shell-less snail. In the breeding season one sea hare mounts another and they mate. Unlike the earthworms they do not exchange sperm. Where the procedure is unusual is that the top sea hare may itself be mounted, so that it is giving sperm to sea hare A and receiving sperm from C. The process becomes somewhat bizarre when as many as seven or eight animals become involved at once, the final touch being when the one at the head of the line swings round to mount the one at the tail, forming a strange reproductive circle.

The importance of cross fertilization to a species is some justification for these antics, and the related land snail also goes to great lengths to ensure reciprocal mating. In fact the mating of the snail has some points in common with that of the leech described earlier in that the sperms are contained in spermatophores and the animals stimulate one another by hypodermic injection. In the case of the snail it is not the spermatophore that is injected: the process is even more complicated. At the end of their reproductive tract snails have a dart sac which contains the dart, a sculptured calcareous weapon, which they can eject at will. When two snails are almost in contact, just prior to mating, they expel their darts with great vigor from the openings of their female ducts into their partners' bodies. These darts enter with such force that they quite often become embedded in the animal's gut or other internal organs. This drastic action seems to provide sexual stimulation and they then approach one another and exchange spermatophores. These are stored in the spermathecae where the covering of the spermatophore is dissolved and the sperm released.

These mating methods may seem crude to the human observer, but those of the dragonfly and little pseudoscorpions are more graceful. Pseudoscorpions are delightful animals, minute relations of the spider, with their first pair of legs modified to form pincers like a lobster's claws. Their mating dance is very complicated and both take part. The male seizes the female by the pincers and holds her while he secretes a spermatophore like the large-headed pins used for sticking in maps. Then he maneuvers himself so that he is holding the spermatophore under her abdomen. When she is ready she opens her sexual pore and takes it into her sperm sac, where the sperms are released so that they can fertilize her waiting eggs.

Both the male and female dragonflies take part in their mating dance. They fly around in pairs, the male leading and grasping the female round the neck with a pair of specially developed abdominal appendages. They usually perform considerable acrobatics before they are ready to mate, but in the end they settle on a twig and the female flexes her abdomen so that it points forward toward the male and she is able to pull the spermatophore out of its special packet on his thorax. He continues to hold her until the sperms have escaped from the spermatophore into her body cavity, finally releasing her so that she can begin to lay her eggs.

Not all female insects behave with such restraint when taking the spermatophore from their mates, for the marine worm platynereis is not alone in regarding the sperms as delectable food. Crickets, grasshoppers and the spongilla fly regard the spermatophore as edible. When the male short-horn grasshopper places the spermatophore in the female's genital opening, one lobe is left protruding and while she devours this the sperms escape from the remainder into her genital tract. The tree cricket tackles the problem differently, feeding the female during mating so her attention is distracted from the spermatophore. If they are disturbed at the time, so that the feeding stops, the female will eat the entire spermatophore and so remain unmated.

Although a spermatophore provides a convenient way of ensuring the safety of the sperms during mating, its transference to the female is often a delicate and lengthy operation. Many animals have avoided this and other disadvantages by the development of the end part of the male's reproductive tract into a special mobile sperm-carrying duct, the penis. There is a corresponding modification of the female's duct to form a special pocket, the vagina, into which the penis fits. These animals can then transfer a fluid suspension of sperm from one to the other in a matter of seconds. Speed is not always essential and, in fact, some animals remain coupled together for long periods of time. The penis is developed in a wide variety of forms in insects, reptiles, birds and mammals. Mammals are the only group where it is found in all males.

Insects, the only invertebrate group to adopt this form of mating, seem to have made the process unnecessarily complicated. In the majority of cases the male penis points backward and the whole organ has to be inverted before it can enter the female's genital opening. This means that mating insects often go through a considerable variety of contortions. The simplest way to achieve a successful mating seems to be for the male to alight on the female's back and curve his abdomen round to introduce the penis into the female's vagina. Some insects do mate in this way, although the males do not always have an easy time. For instance the male horse fly lands on the female's back to mate, but she is apt to fly off in the middle, dragging him with her hanging down backwards and held only by his clasping appendages and penis. Other flies curl their abdomen over their shoulder and approach the female from behind. If the abdomen is very long and flexible they may even mount. The important thing seems to be that the female's body should remain undistorted, while the contortions of the male are of no consequence. This is not the end of the curious ways in which insects choose to mate. Crane flies stand tail to tail, the male's body rotating through an angle of 180 degrees. Sometimes this torsion takes place in the larval stages so that the adults can mate without any additional twisting.

Insects make mating so complicated that it seems a wonder they ever produce any offspring. They have one more refinement in the development of their mating structures. They are the only group of animals where it appears to matter which surface of the penis is uppermost when entering the vagina. Often the structure of their genital organs is so complicated by the presence of bristles, pads and toothlike projections that they act like a lock and key. They can only mate with another of the same species. It seems that the presence of these complex structures on the female's body stimulates her and provides the last vital link in the chain of reactions leading to mating. Lack of this stimulation is a bar to mating and a safeguard against breeding between species.

The insect penis is an armored, inflexible organ, and other structures are usually developed in association with it to ensure that the female's body is clasped in the correct position for mating. Where a penis is present in vertebrates it is generally unarmored and contains spaces in its tissue that can be filled with blood and lymph, making it rigid when occasion demands. Some animals have a penis bone, which gives additional rigidity, and this structure may have developed in animals where mating is unduly prolonged. It is found in such animals as dogs, ferrets, mink, the walrus and whales, to mention but a few.

Both birds and reptiles have internal fertilization and many of them have developed a penis to assist this process. In reptiles it is usually a simple structure, snakes being unusual in having a pair of structures called hemipenes. All flightless birds have a well-developed penis, as do all the ducks, but many other birds manage with a small erectile papilla at the end of the male duct, a small portion of which can be turned inside out during mating.

All mammals have some form of penis; these are of two main types, one being vascular and the other fibro-elastic, with a vast range of intermediate forms linking them. If mating is to be successful the penis must be both rigid and reasonably long when inserted into the female's vagina, but it is easier to protect if at other times it is smaller and flexible. This is achieved by the whole structure becoming rigid and erect only at times of sexual excitement. The penis consists of the terminal portion of the urethra and three large vascular columns of muscle attached at one end to the bones of the pelvic girdle. Erection takes place when the blood vessels in the erectile tissue fill, as a result of the relaxation of the artery walls. The tip of the penis is very sensitive to touch and when stimulated by contact sends impulses through the spinal cord, producing the male orgasm. The muscles of the male duct undergo reflex contractions and the semen, containing the sperm, is ejaculated. Animals with a fibro-elastic penis have very little vascular erectile tissue, rigidity being due to the fibrous connective tissue of which the penis is formed. This type of penis is generally retracted into the body cavity, thus protecting it when the animal is not mating.

The penis has only developed in animals with internal fertilization and although it may also contain the urinary openings, its chief importance is during mating. There are many animals, however, where the organs used for mating are found in both sexes but especially well developed in the male. An example of this is found in both the common octopus and the squid. With the exception of a few species, all octopi and squids have one or more arms modified for mating in the male to form a structure called the hectocotylus. It is used to plant sperm in the female's mantle cavity, the arms that are so developed varying from species to species. In both the lesser and common octopus the end of the third right arm becomes spoon-shaped; in squids the suckers tend to be very reduced or to disappear altogether. The heterocotylized arm usually carries the sperms in one of three ways. In the squids and cuttlefish the slightly modified arm merely takes the spermatophores from the male's genital opening and hands them to the female. In most octopi, the hectocotylized arm is inserted near the female's oviducts, forming a groove down which the sperm may pass. In the argonauts and a few closely related octopi, the hectocotylized arm ends in a thin, wormlike piece which breaks off completely when inserted into the female with the spermatophore and remains behind after mating.

Male spiders have also developed substitutes for a penis. These are the palpal bulbs. In both sexes there is a pair of appendages, beside the jaws and in front of the first pair of walking legs, called the palpi. They are used to manipulate food, and for various other things. Those of the male have a hollow enlargement at the tip. During courtship the male spider spins a web and deposits a small blob of semen on it. He then uses this as a reservoir from which to fill his palpal bulbs. When he dips them in, the semen rises by the combined forces of gravity and capillary action. Then, using these palpal bulbs rather like a fountain pen, he puts them into the female's storage receptacles, empties them and repeats the process until she has sufficient to fertilize all her eggs.

Lobsters and crabs have already been mentioned as having some of their limbs modified for mating, and the common dogfish has modified pelvic fins which act like a penis. They form scroll-like organs which contain erectile tissue, and are inserted into the female cloaca during mating.

Animals mate in so many different ways, depending on their degree of development and their surroundings, yet all these different ways achieve much the same end. There is an interesting example of how these differences may have arisen in the three species of periwinkle found on the seashore. This is a small snail-like animal and the three species most usually found live in very clearly defined zones. They also have completely different ways of mating.

The common periwinkle is found from the top to the bottom of the tidal zone of the shore, the rough periwinkle from the half-tide line to the splash zone at the top of the beach, and the smooth periwinkle from the half-tide line to the low-water mark.

The common periwinkle has the simplest mating habits;

like so many other animals living in the sea, it simply discharges eggs and sperm into the sea in vast numbers at high tide and fertilization is external. Many of the fertilized eggs are lost, but some drift about and finally settle on the shore.

The smooth periwinkle, at the bottom of the shore, lays

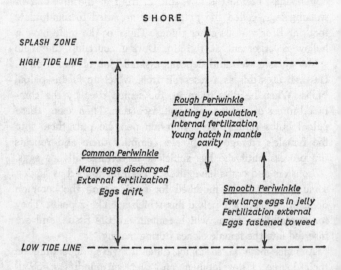

SHORE

SPLASH ZONE
HIGH TIDE LINE

Rough Periwinkle
Mating by copulation.
Internal fertilization
Young hatch in mantle cavity

Common Periwinkle
Many eggs discharged
External fertilization
Eggs drift

Smooth Periwinkle
Few large eggs in jelly
Fertilization external
Eggs fastened to weed

LOW TIDE LINE

SEA

[2] *The relation between the pattern of reproduction and habitat in periwinkles.*

fewer, larger eggs. They are enclosed in small masses of jelly and fastened to weeds. Fertilization is still external but happens where they are spawned. They may still be killed by heat or dessication, but if they survive they are in the right place to develop. The rough periwinkles are faced with the problems common to all animals living high up on the shore. They are constantly in danger of getting too dry and must be able to exist as both land and sea animals. Consequently they have internal fertilization, the male having a simple penis and mating by copulation. The fertilized eggs are protected by an egg case, which is kept in the mantle cavity until the young hatch and settle beside the mother.

There would be no point in developing special organs for mating if this development were not accompanied by an innate knowledge of how to use them. Mating is the culmination of a complex chain of events. Each step has a logical sequence. If any step is blocked, then the sequence of events is broken and mating is unlikely to take place. In the higher vertebrates the sex drive that impels mating behavior depends on the internal condition of the individual, the hormones acting on the central nervous system. When the nervous system is so sensitized, the animal responds to the stimulus offered by the secondary sexual characters of the opposite sex. The picture becomes complicated because it is hard to define to what extent sexual behavior is conditioned or learned.

Similarly a male with a high output of male hormones will react earlier to a female in heat than a male with a low level of male hormones. Successful mating also requires the cooperation of the female and the normal functioning of her reproductive organs. As in the male, her pattern of sexual behavior also depends on hormonal influences and the stimulation of her senses.

There are many ways of bringing ova and sperm together in space and time, which is the primary function of mating. The animals which so differ in their ways of mating must also differ in their genetical make-up. This diversity can only have arisen by mutation and natural selection. The balance between fertility and infertility is a very critical one for any species. Any mutation which affects this balance will have a direct effect by determining the number of progeny in subsequent generations. The delicacy of this balance may be responsible for the wide variety of reproductive organs and mating patterns. The general tendency of evolution has been toward the development of internal fertilization. What are the advantages of this system? It is far more complicated than simply releasing the sex cells, sperms or ova, and this must be justified to make it worth while. The emphasis in higher vertebrates seems to be on quality rather than quantity. The female cod lays four million eggs, only a few of which reach maturity. The mammals tend to develop one or two eggs at a time, a high percentage of which reach breeding age. More young survive because they get more parental care, right from internal fertilization, through the development of the embryo within the parent's body, until some time after birth. In man, the fact that such a high percentage of young survive has brought a new crop of problems, not the least of which is the one of overpopulation.

7

Is Sex Necessary?

The term sexual reproduction implies, quite rightly, that there is an alternative. Both animals and plants can reproduce without sex, that is to say asexually. Some of the problems of sexual reproduction have already been discussed. It may involve elaborate courtship, and the actual mechanical business of mating is often a masterpiece of zoological engineering. If asexual reproduction avoids some of these complications, why is it not more widely used?

Reproduction can be with or without sex. What then is sex? It is a word often heard nowadays and its everyday interpretation tends to be somewhat different from its scientific meaning. When scientists talk of sex, they are referring to the fact that the majority of living animals can be divided into two groups, males and females, with different reproductive functions and attributes. In some animals and plants these two sets of characters are combined in one individual which is then called a hermaphrodite, but except in this instance it is necessary to have one of each sort to achieve sexual reproduction. Man is exceptional in that the sexual act of coition has acquired a significance of its own in the pattern of human behavior; it is no longer simply the culmination of one part of the reproductive cycle. Sex novels, sex crimes and sex appeal are convenient expressions implying that the differences between the male and female have some bearing on the subject being discussed. What purposes do these differ-

ences serve? Before this can be answered the alternatives
must be investigated.

The essence of multiplication is the creation of additional
individuals. It is sometimes very difficult to distinguish multiplication from growth; the dividing line is very fine. Some very
simple animals live together in groups or colonies and, although they are joined together, are nevertheless a collection
of individuals. They are able to multiply by budding, and if
one member of the colony is damaged it is able to make good
the injury by a form of growth called regeneration. In the
first case a new individual has been created. In the second
there has merely been a repair to one damaged individual, in
the same way that a growth of new skin repairs a cut finger.
So far so good, but if a flatworm is cut in two, the head will
grow a new tail and the tail a new head. There are now two
worms, and the injury to both halves has been repaired. Is
this process asexual reproduction or regeneration?

This sort of unanswerable problem does not arise with sexual reproduction, whose features make it quite distinctly a
method of multiplication. All sexual reproduction involves
fusion between males and females, but this fusion can only
take place on the level of single cells with one nucleus each.
This means that the more complex animals, made up of many
cells, have to produce special cells for this fusion process.
These are the sex cells or gametes. Both types of sex cell
may be produced by one animal, but generally the sexes are
separate.

If the reproduction process involves one individual it is obviously simpler than a method involving two, and this sim-
plicity is presumably an advantage. Plants make wide use of
asexual reproduction, many examples of which are well
known to the gardener. Strawberry runners, blackberry stolons, auxiliary tulip bulbs are all examples of asexual reproduction, while seaweeds and fungi are able quite simply
to split in two.

In some cases the methods are more elaborate, as when special cells or spores are produced. The edible mushroom, for example, is only the fruiting body, or spore bearer, of the fungus, the main body of which is the ramifying mass of microscopic threads of cells called the mycelium, which lies beneath the ground. These threads of fungus tissue grow rapidly and by this means the fungus can spread itself through the soil. Why then do fungi produce spores? They serve two purposes, either to provide a means of dispersal or to resist bad external conditions which might destroy the parent plant. Not all fungi produce both types of spore, and the mushroom contains only the dispersal type. Such spores may be dispersed by wind or water, depending on the parent plant. The "resistant" spores are able to remain dormant and unharmed during periods of unfavorable conditions and can then develop into new plants when things return to normal.

Do animals make as much use of asexual reproduction as plants? The problems that face the two main groups of living things are very different. The majority of animals live a free existence, even if their range is limited. The majority of plants are fixed. For plants the problem of dispersal is a pressing one and asexual reproduction is an admirable means of "spreading." It is interesting that the most highly developed group of animals to reproduce asexually is that of the sea squirts or tunicates, the majority of which remain in the same place all their lives, attached to a wharf or the bottom of a ship. A great many invertebrates have some means of reproducing asexually, but their methods are only ancillary to the principal sexual methods. The simpler the type of animal, the commoner the asexual method is, and among the vertebrates it is extremely unusual. In fact the only form of asexual reproduction in vertebrates is called polyembryony, which is the production of two or more individuals from one fertilized egg. It can, therefore, only take place after sexual reproduction. Normally the fertilized egg develops by dividing into first two, then four cells and so on until a complicated individual of millions of cells has developed. In polyembryony the first division completely splits the egg, forming two halves which then develop in the normal way. The most successful exponent of polyembryony is the six-banded armadillo. These quaint, heavily plated creatures are found in South America and with their armored appearance seem like some relic of prehistoric times. For some reason they produce identical quadruplets from each fertilized egg, although the advantages of this process are somewhat obscure. Man, among other mammals, occasionally follows their example, since identical twins are also the result of an egg having multiplied asexually to give two individuals instead of one. Since sex is decided at the time of fertilization, identical twins must always be two girls or two boys. Twins of different sexes have always come from two eggs. There is at least one case in England of identical quadruplets, and they are the result of the egg's having divided twice before development began. No doubt they would be surprised to know how much they have in common with the six-banded armadillo.

Simple animals and plants split in two, but the splitting of plumose anemones is spectacular and their cells must have remained very adaptable for the process to be successful. The two parts of the basal disc start to glide in opposite directions, causing the central column to become constricted and finally to break in two longitudinally. There are then two anemones where only a short while before there was one. This is not their only trick; they can go one better on occasions. Here they contract, pulling in the basal disc but leaving behind a ring of small bits of basal tissue. In two weeks or a little more these pieces of basal disc are able to grow a mouth and tentacles, forming a new anemone. The Japanese anemones multiply the same way in principle, but the method is different. They can throw off their tentacles and grow a new set; this is regeneration. The discarded tentacles do not just wither, but after growing a bit become new individuals. This is reproduction, but the processes are very similar indeed and are reminiscent of the flatworm.

[3] *A side view of the sea anemone in the process of fission. The oral discs and part of the central column have already divided and shortly the central column will be completely separated. After drawings by Louis Agassiz.*

It is easy enough to accept the idea of one cell splitting in half, even though it is remarkable that the halves are identical down to the last detail. It seems the logical way to multiply. The idea of fission becomes far more intriguing when it is found to be used by an animal like the flatworm, which has a simple brain and central nervous system.

The splitting of organized nerve tracts must be a very delicate operation. In summer some flatworms shed their tails and grow new ones and the tails grow new heads. In the laboratory some worms have been sliced into as many as five or six bits, each of which became a complete individual. These animals' cells are obviously far more adaptable than those of man. If a man cuts himself he will, in time, grow new cells to repair the cut; he cannot, however, grow a new finger or toe, let alone an arm or a leg. His powers of regeneration are very limited and never faintly approximate a method of reproduction. However, there are a number of worms which can either split off portions of themselves or which can grow extensions which split off later. These worms are divided into segments and this seems to make the splitting

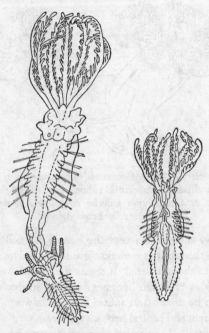

[4] *The worm Salmacina undergoing fission. The drawing at the left shows the beginning of the formation of a new zooid at the hind end of the parent worm. At the right, the zooid has separated from the parent worm and is beginning its independent life. After Huxley.*

off process easier, in the same way that it is easier to break some squares off a block of chocolate than it is to break squares in half. There are a number of different ways of reproducing by fission, but the worm Salmacina is typical of the group. When the worm is ready to divide, a constriction appears near the tail and develops the beginning of a new set of head appendages. The part behind the outgrowths becomes a distinct structure called a zooid, which breaks off and eventually grows the full adult number of segments. Some worms go even further, developing a series of constrictions until they look like a string of sausages. They make the new segments near the tail and these are then separated by a constriction. Fresh segments appear in front of the constriction, the process being repeated until there is a string of zooids. Finally they all break off and each grows into an adult worm. One worm even forms lateral branches like the mycelium of a fungus. This worm, Syllis ramosa, is found inside deep-water sponges and its laterally branching zooids give it a strangely tangled appearance.

Plants have found budding a satisfactory method of increasing their stock, and animals that live like plants, in one place, have made equal use of it. The sponges, which at first glance look like mosses or lichens, make simple external buds while the fresh-water sponges have their buds internally. (The buds are then called gemmules.)

These gemmules are somewhat similar to the seeds of plants, and are formed inside the sponge toward the end of the year. They are a round group of cells enclosed in an envelope which may have peculiarly shaped spikes in it, and they are set free when a bit of the sponge decays. They fall to the bottom and nothing more happens to them for the whole winter. In the spring the envelope breaks open and the ball of cells escapes to the outside, where it grows, in due course, into an adult sponge. This delayed development to overcome bad conditions is not peculiar to asexual reproduction, nor is it by any means the only reason for it. Asexual reproduction is more often used as a means of multiplication, pure and simple.

Despite all these systems, some animals are not content.

Asexual reproduction has certain drawbacks and so they use both methods, sexual and asexual. Part of their life they reproduce one way and part the other. This alternation is particularly typical of parasitic animals. One such animal is the liver fluke, well known to farmers and vets. It is a parasite of both sheep and snails, and while nobody minds much what it does to snails, they do provide a means of controlling the fluke, since it can't live without them. The liver fluke reproduces sexually, but sexual reproduction does not produce a sufficient quantity of offspring, so it uses asexual methods as well. The life history, like that of most parasites, is complicated and includes several larval stages. In two of these stages the larvae can speed up the process by multiplying asexually. In this way a few fertilized eggs can produce a large number of individuals and the chances of reaching another host animal are greatly increased.

It is surprisingly the ascidians that have developed a num-

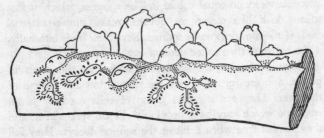

[5] *Part of a colony of the ascidian Metandrocarpa taylori, growing on a tube of a marine worm. The older zooids are in the background. Tubelike outgrowths are forming from two of these. The new zooids arise from these outgrowths by budding—an example of asexual reproduction. After a drawing by Donald P. Abbott.*

ber of ways of dividing asexually—surprisingly, because the ascidians are a strange group of marine creatures, superficially like sea anemones, and in fact closely related to the first simple vertebrates. They can split down the middle and they can also form buds, the methods of budding being extremely varied. The vast majority also reproduce sexually, but their ability to divide rapidly must be a great help in increasing their range since many of them are either sedentary or float helplessly at the mercy of the currents.

At first glance there is little to support the theory that the ascidians are closely related to the simplest vertebrates, but zoologists who have studied them, and particularly their larvae, are sure this is the case. These larvae are very distinctive and are similar to the fishlike groups of vertebrates, rather than the lower invertebrates. Some ascidians are solitary, others establish large colonies. These colonies are formed by budding and come in all shapes and sizes. Budding generally takes place from a stolon, which is an outgrowth from the abdominal region of the parent. In the simple colonial forms the individuals remain joined by the stolon, while in the more complex colonies all the animals are joined in a common covering with only their mouths and excretory openings reaching the outside world. In this case the connection with the stolon is lost. Most solitary forms also originate from a stolon but break away instead of remaining attached to the parent. The most interesting thing about the ascidians' budding is that the structure of the stolon, from which the buds come, is usually very simple. The cells which form the internal organs of the buds bear very little relation to the type of cell which formed the embryonic organs of the parent. Gut cells are not needed to provide gut in the bud. The cells of the stolon have retained the power of developing into different organs even though they come from an adult animal. In all but one group of ascidians, sexual and asexual reproduction is linked, and the sexual forms are capable of only asexual reproduction and vice versa. This ensures that the generations alternate. This is the most complex group of animals to have asexual reproduction as an essential and integral feature of its life cycle. It is only possible because the body structure of the adults is far simpler than their position in the classification of animals would suggest. They do show that it is an extremely efficient way for a simple stationary animal to colonize large areas of the sea bed.

The ascidians come near the top of the invertebrate kingdom in the zoological classification. At the other end of the scale come the bacteria. These minute organisms take many different shapes and forms and are known, like the ascidians, to have several different ways of multiplying. For some time now bacteria have been known to split in various ways, just as the protozoans and worms divide. Now it seems they have other methods of reproduction which are neither asexual nor sexual. Asexual reproduction is when a single living unit divides into two or more parts, which then lead independent lives; sexual reproduction is when two units co-operate to produce one or more others. These living units may be multicelled anemones or single sex cells; the process is the same. The microscopic bacteria and viruses do things differently. Generally the products of asexual reproduction are exactly like the parent; an individual produced by sexual reproduction will be different, having some characters from each parent. A bacterium can, alone, give rise to a new strain. In spite of the fact that bacteria and viruses have a very simple biological structure, chemically they are extremely complicated. A bacterium may contain over a thousand kinds of protein; these are made up of chemical units called amino acids, and the proportions and arrangements of these amino acids differ from bacterium to bacterium. Very little is known about the way in which the amino acids are assembled into proteins, so that many bacterial processes are still a mystery. Much of what follows really falls in the province of biochemistry, but a number of discoveries about bacteria and their ways of reproduction are fundamental to the whole of biology.

A bacterium can give rise to a new strain by taking up a

single molecule, corresponding to a gene, and this is then copied in subsequent divisions, becoming a hereditary character. A single molecule can also be carried over by a virus, again producing a new strain. The results are what one would expect from sexual reproduction but only a single bacterium or virus is involved.

This is not the limit of the exceptional ways of bacteria and viruses. New strains of bacteria can be formed by a process of transformation. Transformation is a word reminiscent of fairy godmothers, but the changes that occur in bacteria are no less remarkable. Bacteria of one strain exposed to living or dead members of another strain may develop some of the latter's characteristics. This seems like a pregnant woman's spending nine months at the horse races and then producing a champion jockey.

A type of bacterium known to undergo transformation is the pneumococci. The capsules of these bacteria are formed of complex chains of molecules called polysaccharides, and different types of pneumococci have different polysaccharides in their capsules. If a strain of pneumococci is killed, it can be used to provide a solution called a transforming principle. This transforming principle will convert one strain to another, namely to the strain from which it was prepared. This is rather like dyeing a piece of cloth. If it is soaked in a blue dye it turns blue. The fascinating thing about bacteria is that while the process seems a chemical one, they can then go on reproducing as this new strain in the normal way. One strain can even be treated with two transforming principles and form an entirely new strain, combining two sets of characters in one single form.

Transformation is peculiar to bacteria but is not the only way they make new strains. Bacteria are also known to undergo recombination. This was first described by Lederberg and Tatum in 1946, who watched it in a strain called Escherichia coli. Pairs of individual cells mate, forming a narrow connecting bridge of cytoplasm, the basic material of cellular matter. It is presumably through this bridge that genetic material passes from one cell to the other. A strange series of facts then emerged. Another research worker, Hayes, found that recombination still went on after one parent strain had been "killed." Killed in this sense means so damaged by ultraviolet radiation that the cells can no longer divide. Those strains that still act as parents after killing are called "donors" and those that are unable to are called "recipients." It was found that when two donor strains were brought together there were only a few recombinations, while two recipient strains gave none. A donor and a recipient strain together gave the highest percentage of recombinations, and the cytoplasm for recombination came mainly from the recipient. This is similar to the female sex cells of all higher animals which are passive and contribute most of the cytoplasm to the future embryo. The capacity to be a donor can be transferred to the recipient strains by simple contact. If the passive recipient is like the female cell, then the active donor is like the male cell. So it would appear that some bacteria have the characters of maleness which can be "caught" by other bacteria like a contagious disease. Perhaps this is an evolutionary stage between sexual reproduction and some of the asexual processes peculiar to bacteria. In some ways bacteria behave like the genes, or units of heredity, of higher animals. They can gain and lose characters in a single step and there is no reason why "maleness" should not be among these characters. It is difficult to imagine a stage intermediate between sexual and asexual reproduction. Either a male and female cell or unit combine to give rise to a new individual, in which case it is sexual reproduction, or only one unit or individual is involved, in which case it is asexual. Bacteria have already shown that they can acquire new characters, even when only one unit is involved, by taking up a molecule and copying it, or by the action of a transforming principle. Already there are systems that have differences from the straightforward divisions of asexual reproduction, and they are the nearest living things come to a halfway stage. Sexual reproduction provides variation among those it produces. Briefly this variation is due to the combination of characters contributed by the two parents. A normal cell contains a nucleus. This nucleus has a set of paired rod-like structures called chromosomes, which carry the genes responsible for the individual's heredity. When the chromosomes are present in pairs the nucleus is called "diploid." For reasons explained later, it is essential that sex cells contain only half the normal number of chromosomes, and these nuclei are called "haploid." In sexual reproduction the haploid male nucleus and the haploid female nucleus combine at fertilization to give a diploid nucleus. This nucleus has a set of chromosomes from each parent. During subsequent development it divides repeatedly and grows into an animal or plant with some characters from one parent and some from the other.

So far it has been apparent that animals who reproduce asexually have a certain advantage over those who do not. Even so, it is very rarely the only method of reproduction employed by a species; apart from the Protozoa and some of the simplest plants, every living thing reproduces sexually at some stage during its life. Sometimes things are so arranged that an animal has two forms, one capable only of asexual reproduction giving rise to one capable of sexual reproduction. This produces regular alternation of sexual and asexual generation. Other animals resort to sexual reproduction only when living conditions are difficult. The animals and plants who get most benefit from asexual reproduction seem to be those that multiply this way when living conditions are good, but can easily switch to sexual methods if conditions deteriorate. These animals can take advantage of the fact that there is more than enough food available in spring and summer to support large numbers of their kind. With the coming of autumn and the dwindling of food supplies they produce a sexual form which in time produces a fertilized egg. This egg is often specially resistant to unfavorable conditions and is able to survive the winter without developing further. Development restarts the following spring and the cycle begins all over again.

The key to survival in both plants and animals is adaptability to changing conditions. All living things produced by asexual reproduction will have a uniform genetic inheritance, apart from new forms which are the result of an occasional gene mutation. When the sea anemone sheds its tentacles and they grow into new anemones, they are all identical genetically. The flatworms produced by slicing up one worm are all identical. The strawberry plants that grow from runners or the blackberries that develop from stolons are identical with the parent plants. In sexual reproduction the essence of the whole process is the fusion of male and female sex cells to give an offspring with an entirely new genetic constitution, part inherited from the mother and part from the father. Plants which reproduce sexually, the flowering plants for example, will produce a terrific variation of offspring since they may be fertilized with a variety of pollen. Incidentally gardeners and horticulturists do not always welcome this variation. A number of plants produce such variable seedlings that they are valueless commercially; in these cases the gardener or grower resorts to artificial asexual reproduction. By cuttings, or artificially rooted shoots, and grafting he persuades the plant to reproduce vegetatively and so builds up a uniform stock. This is the only way to ensure that the roses offered for sale are what they claim to be and the only way a winegrower can get a field of identical vines. It is also a useful way of propagating slow-growing plants which take years to mature from seed. By propagating them artificially and making them reproduce vegetatively the number of plants can be increased in a far shorter time.

Similarly marine animals that just release eggs and sperm into the surrounding sea, like codfish and sea urchins, will produce a very variable new generation. Even animals which are hermaphrodite, that is having male and female organs in the same individual, very rarely resort to self-fertilization. They often avoid this by one set of sex organs developing before the other, or, as in the earthworm, the male and female organs are so placed in the body that it is easier for the worm to mate with another individual than to fertilize itself. It is a waste of time to go to the trouble of developing sexual organs if they are then used for self-fertilization, since this produces no more variation in the offspring than asexual reproduction would have done.

The reproductive habits of the Protozoa reflect, to a certain extent, the general trend of development throughout the animal kingdom. As the complexity of the cell increases, sexual reproduction tends to replace asexual methods. In some forms this has proved an unnecessary complication and there has been a subsequent return to asexual methods, or a simplification of the sexual processes. Sexual reproduction in a protozoan population seems to lead to increased vigor.

Living things reproduce asexually, bisexually and also monosexually. This latter is the famous virgin birth. This is generally a misnomer in the animal kingdom, since the females concerned are not necessarily virgins and are capable of reproducing with a male one time and without one the next. It is perhaps more accurate to call the process by its scientific name of parthenogenesis. Honeybees are among the best-known exponents of this process, which has economic importance since it is a feature of the lives of such plagues as greenfly and phylloxera or vine louse. It is claimed that true virgin birth has taken place in the human race, but so far without any convincing scientific proof.

The fact that greenfly can become such a serious pest in so short a time is due to their parthenogenetic development. The story starts with a single female in spring and the situation does not appear serious. But she has no need of a male, and soon she is surrounded by her offspring, small replicas of their mother. They have grown from the eggs she laid and are all females. In a short while they too have begun to lay eggs and their numbers increase relentlessly. Normally, unfertilized eggs contain only half the number of chromosomes found in an ordinary body cell; they are haploid. Greenfly females produce diploid eggs with the same number of chromosomes as every other cell, and they develop into females. Soon there is a vast population of identical female greenflies laying eggs and feeding on the young leaves which are plentiful in spring and summer. Toward the end of the season there is a change. The females start to lay haploid eggs, with a single set of chromosomes. These eggs develop into males. At the end of the season both males and females are winged and the females continue to lay haploid eggs. When these are fertilized they give a fertilized diploid egg which will eventually develop into a female and start the whole cycle off once more. The introduction of a bisexual stage at the end of the summer serves two purposes. For one thing the fertilized egg remains dormant the whole winter and provides a means of surviving those hard times; for another thing the females produced from the fertilized eggs get a set of chromosomes from their mother and one from their father, and so a valuable source of variation is introduced into the animal's life cycle.

It is somewhat daunting to picture the myriads of identical greenfly descended from one squat female. Phylloxera, which is related to the greenfly, has made things infinitely more complicated. This little animal has been the scourge of the vineyards of Europe since 1863, and its methods of re-

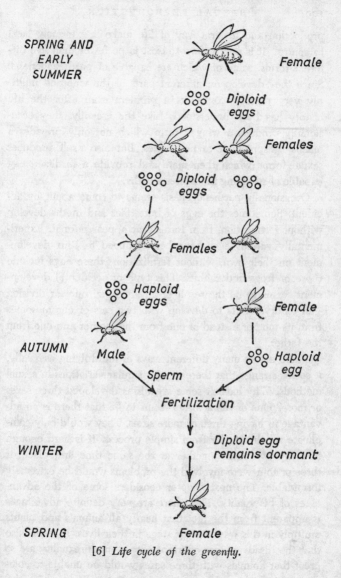

[6] *Life cycle of the greenfly.*

production and general way of life make it extremely hard to control. It is now known to exist in no fewer than five different forms, some of which are capable of parthenogenesis. Since they develop on different parts of the vine and multiply very rapidly, control is a problem even after the life history has been understood. Like the greenfly, they occasionally produce a winged form which not only provides a means of spreading to new vines, but also itself produces sexual forms which then mate and provide a fertilized egg capable of surviving the winter months.

Occasionally parthenogenesis seems to come about by accident. Sometimes the eggs of butterflies and moths develop without fertilization, from forms that appear normal. Experimentally various eggs have been induced to start development on their own, without fertilization; these eggs include those of frogs and rabbits. This type of accidental development seems to be the result of an abnormal nuclear division —an embryo starts to develop with two sets of chromosomes from its mother instead of one from the mother and one from the father.

There are so many different ways of multiplying asexually, it seems strange that there are not similar variations in sexual methods. Why haven't some organisms developed three sexes or more? One of the answers seems to be that there is no advantage in having three or more sexes. They would only complicate an already far from simple process. It is hard enough to bring two sexes together at the same time and place; if three or four were involved the problems would be extremely formidable. The next chapter considers some of the advantages of bisexuality. That there are very definite advantages is apparent from the fact that nearly all animals and plants multiply in this way at some stage in their lives. It seems also that the disadvantages of trisexuality or multisexuality are so great that animals with three sexes would be unable to compete successfully with their bisexual rivals and would be eliminated.

Insects seem able to live in every nook and cranny from the seashore to the tops of mountains, from lush jungles to such unlikely places as the oil puddles on American oil fields. What is the explanation of their success? Is it connected with their ways of reproducing? As with so many biological questions there is no simple, cut-and-dried answer. What is certain is that their ways of reproduction have not hindered their spread. The sexes are separate and distinct with one notable exception. This is a self-fertilizing hermaphrodite called Icerya purchasi. Its name is unimportant but it is unique in its class and how or why it has arisen is a mystery. The vast majority of insects reproduce sexually, laying yolky eggs after copulation. They are generally very prolific and lay vast numbers of eggs in their lifetime. The inevitable exceptions are provided by those insects whose young are born alive, such as the tsetse fly, and those who have developed some new slant on the normal procedure. The greenflies multiply rapidly by the misnamed virgin birth, and the chalcid wasps imitate the armadillos, only instead of producing four offspring from one egg they provide no fewer than a hundred. In the end the great secret of the success of insects seems to lie not in the many ways they have of reproducing asexually, but in the fact that they use these methods to augment sexual reproduction, never to replace it.

Every type of reproduction involves some degree of loss of parental material and, therefore, entails physiological strain. Both the strain and the loss of material are far greater in asexual reproduction than in any form of sexual reproduction. One of the advantages of asexual reproduction is the lack of larval and embryonic stages in the life history of those who have adopted it as their main method of multiplying, since both these are very vulnerable phases in any pattern of development. The fact that it is not more widespread, and is impracticable for vertebrates, seems to indicate that the advantages it offers are not sufficient to outweigh the disadvantages. Over the millions of years in which living things are known to have evolved and developed, sexual reproduction has proved the most satisfactory method.

8

The Advantages of Sexual Reproduction

Living matter consists of individual organisms which will eventually die. The continuance of life depends on their capacity for reproduction. The simpler plants and animals reproduce with great rapidity by uncomplicated asexual methods. This means they do not have vulnerable embryonic or larval stages in their life history, nor do they need to develop complex reproductive structures. Generally, the the whole body is involved in this act of reproduction. While this presents no great problems to a single-celled organism, like a protozoan or a unicellular algae, it is obviously a wildly impracticable method for a giraffe or a codfish. Secondly, if an animal or plant of more than one cell is going to reproduce asexually, its cells must remain very adaptable in order to form the various organs of the new individual. Bud formation would be impossible if the bud had to contain every type of specialized cell needed in an adult. In the last chapter the flatworms were mentioned as being able to grow new parts even when cut into five or six slices. Although this is remarkable, a flatworm is still a comparatively simple animal. The more highly developed an animal's brain and central nervous system become, the less likely it is to be able to grow new parts. In fact a few very flexible cells are all that are required and they develop in a number of different ways.

Sexual reproduction removes the need for this adaptability. Where it is used, the only cells that need to keep their plasticity are the sex cells or gametes, and their production is limited to special organs in the body cavity, the gonads. There are definite advantages in limiting the production of sex cells to these sex organs. It has the same effect as the decentralization of a large business or factory: some of the responsibility can be shared. On a cellular level only a few highly specialized cells need be ready to develop into a new individual, and in bisexual animals the male and female can share the job of defending and feeding the young.

The fusion of sex cells is also remarkable. If they were made the same as ordinary cells, then on fusion the new cell would have twice the ordinary number of chromosomes, one set from each parent. But in fact they are different. Somehow they have evolved a method of development which means that they have half the normal chromosome number.

Before the principal advantage of sexual reproduction can be appreciated, it is necessary to know what goes on inside a sex cell prior to maturation, and to envisage the changes at, and after, fertilization.

Cell division goes on all the time in living things, being an essential part of growth and reproduction. Even when an adult man has stopped growing, cell division continues, the processes ranging from the healing of cuts to the ordinary growth of hair and nails. The processes that go on during these divisions are little different from the cell divisions of the Protozoa. In both cases the complicated part of the procedure is the division of the cell nucleus, which is called mitosis.

The cell is sometimes considered the basic unit from which all the more complex living things are elaborated. It is like a brick which can be used in a huge variety of ways to build up an enormous range of structures, the animals and plants. The cell is not just a uniform mass of living matter, but contains a number of organs and inclusions, the most important of which is the nucleus. It is rather like a child's nest of cups or tubs, each one containing one smaller than itself. The cell contains the nucleus and the nucleus, which is bounded by a membrane, contains, among other things, the chromosomes. These chromosomes are a diffuse mass of paired threadlike structures, and to continue the analogy with the nesting tubs, they are not the smallest tub. Chemically known to be made of long chains of protein molecules and nucleic acids, they carry the genes, which are the material units of heredity. It seems incredible, since these are only a few of the structures found in a cell, that division can go on all the time. But such is the case. It goes on in such a way that all the nuclear and cell material is distributed equally between the daughter cells.

Chromosomes change, both in their chemical composition and their reactions to strains, during cell division. This has made it possible to study their behavior under the microscope. When the nucleus divides, the structures inside it must divide too. These include the chromosomes and the chromomeres, where the genes are localized, together with the centromeres, which actually direct the operation of splitting. Cellular division normally follows directly on nuclear division, so that cells soon return to their usual state of one nucleus per cell.

The result of this whole complicated business is to produce two daughter cells with identical genetic compositions, both to each other and the parent cell. This is obviously important during the ordinary process of growth, since if cells of different genetical composition were produced, the individual as a whole would become a queer conglomeration of different groups of cells.

During the resting phase of mitosis the cell appears more or less uniform throughout. The beginning of the first stage of division is noticeable because the chromosomes appear, under the microscope, as double threadlike structures. The two halves, or threads, of the chromosomes are linked at the centromere, and each thread is called a chromatid. The total number of chromosomes found in a normal resting cell is called the diploid number. During the first phase of mitosis the chromosomes change in appearance, becoming shorter and fatter, and a structure called the spindle is formed. This starts as fine lines radiating out from two structures called the centrioles, to form two starlike bodies which then separate to opposite sides of the nucleus. The "rays" from the star stretch out and the whole thing is called the spindle. While

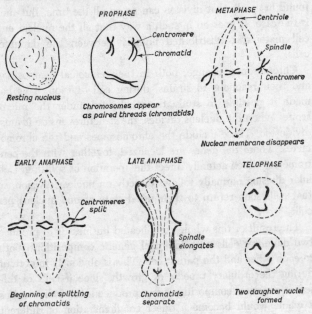

PROPHASE

Centromere

Chromatid

Resting nucleus

Chromosomes appear as paired threads (chromatids)

METAPHASE

Centriole

Spindle

Centromere

Nuclear membrane disappears

EARLY ANAPHASE

Centromeres split

LATE ANAPHASE

Spindle elongates

TELOPHASE

Beginning of splitting of chromatids

Chromatids separate

Two daughter nuclei formed

Chromatids of prophase are chromosomes of telophase

[7] Mitosis.

all this is going on the nuclear membrane disappears and the chromosomes lose water and become closely coiled before attaching themselves to the spindle. This forms the prophase of mitosis and is closely followed by the metaphase. The chromosomes now come to lie in a plane across the equator of the spindle. During the anaphase that follows, the centromere, where the two chromatids were joined, splits and the halves repulse one another, going to opposite poles of the spindle. At the same time the central spindle itself becomes elongated and compressed, as if squeezed by an invisible hand, which helps the two halves of the chromosome to separate. In the final telophase the chromatids reach the two poles and the nucleus is now ready to complete the division into two. The chromatids are now reckoned to be daughter chromosomes. During the subsequent resting phase they become paired structures, appearing as such at the beginning of the next mitotic prophase. A nuclear membrane forms round each set of chromosomes, so two daughter nuclei are formed with the diploid number of chromosomes identical with the parent nucleus. The time taken by a nuclear division varies between some minutes and several hours; the resting phase that follows can be very much longer.

This type of cell division is found in much the same form in all living cells. The division that is responsible for the formation of sex cells is very different. It is called meiosis. It is in fact two divisions, the second following closely on the first. At the end of one of these meiotic divisions a daughter nucleus contains only half the normal number of chromosomes and is called haploid. During meiosis there is also a rearrangement of the material in the chromosomes themselves. The resultant daughter nuclei are no longer identical with each other and the parent nucleus, as they were after mitosis.

Meiosis may be broadly divided into three stages, each containing several phases. During the first stage the chromosomes pair; next they may exchange partners, and in the third and final stage they separate, taking the new partner with them. This exchange of partners during meiosis is the key to the majority of genetical variations and is vitally important.

The prophase in meiosis is much more complicated than in mitosis and is divided into a number of substages. It is during this phase that the number of chromosomes in the nucleus is halved. At the beginning of the prophase the diploid number of chromosomes appear as single unpaired threads; they then come to lie together in pairs, forming the haploid number of paired threads. These paired threads are called bivalents. During the next phase, prior to one of the most important phases of the prophase itself, they become coiled round each other. The chromosomes can now be seen to consist of a pair of chromatids, as in mitosis, so that each bivalent is made up of four threads. As the chromosomes forming the bivalents begin to separate, the chromatids from opposite partners in the bivalent may become crossed. The point where they cross is called a chiasmata, and the chromatids break at the chiasmata, so that when the bivalent later separates, its chromatids may have exchanged portions with those of its opposite number in the other chromosome. This is extremely important because it means that the chromosomes at the end of the prophase of meiosis may have a different genetic constitution from those at the beginning. By the end of the prophase the chromosomes are very short and once more evenly distributed through the nucleus.

The prophase is followed by the first metaphase, which is very similar to the metaphase in mitosis. The nuclear membrane disappears, a spindle is formed and the chromosomes come to lie equidistant above and below it in its equatorial plane. The centromeres of each pair of chromatids, where they are joined, then move to opposite poles of the spindle. This unravels the chiasmata and two daughter nuclei are formed at the poles, while the chromosomes uncoil.

There may now be a resting phase before the second division, which is a simple operation. Here the two chromatids of each chromosome are widely separated, only held together by their centromere. They become distributed about the spin-

dle that forms in each daughter nucleus, and then separate.
Finally four daughter nuclei are formed. Each of these has
half the normal number of chromosomes, or is haploid. These
chromosomes are generally different, genetically, from those

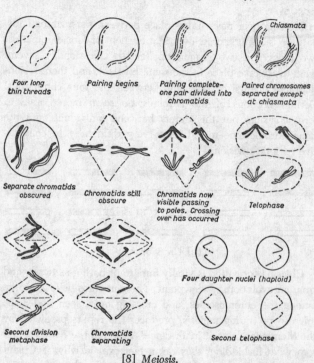

Four long
thin threads

Pairing begins

Pairing complete—
one pair divided into
chromatids

Chiasmata

Paired chromosomes
separated except
at chiasmata

Separate chromatids
obscured

Chromatids still
obscure

Chromatids now
visible passing
to poles. Crossing
over has occurred

Telophase

Second division
metaphase

Chromatids
separating

Four daughter nuclei (haploid)

Second telophase

[8] *Meiosis.*

of the parent. The reduction in the number of chromosomes
during meiosis comes about because the centromere fails to
divide during the first of the two divisions, and instead of one
chromatid's passing to each pole, the pair of chromatids go to
the same pole. Very little is known about the processes that
control the attraction and repulsion of chromosomes, chromatids and centromeres during meiosis and mitosis. However,

the chromosomes in the salivary glands of Drosophila larvae, the fruit fly, are particularly large and suitable for study under the microscope, and they have provided a quantity of information about what happens to chromosomes when they cross over.

Crossing over never takes place between sister chromatids. If there is a single cross over in a bivalent of four chromatids, two cross and two remain unaffected. Occasionally several cross overs take place in the same bivalent, and there is considerable change of segments between the four chromatids. Certain portions of the chromosome seem more liable to form chiasma, but this differs between individuals and the same chromosome may behave very differently in consecutive meiotic divisions.

[9] *Cross over.*

Chiasma formation is vitally important both genetically and from an evolutionary viewpoint. The genes are believed to lie among the chromosomes, and crossing over, seen under the microscope during meiosis, produces the results predicted by the Mendelian laws of inheritance. Although these laws sound somewhat forbidding, they do in fact explain why, if a plant with red flowers is crossed with one with white flowers, a plant with pink flowers will be produced. If two of these pink-flowered plants are then crossed together they will give plants with red, white and pink flowers in definite, predictable proportions. The probability and percentage of these changes are the province of geneticists, but, to come back to meiosis, the genes are exchanged during the crossing-over process.

Crossing over has played an important part in evolution, since it produces changes in the hereditary characters of an individual. Groups of genes linked together are broken up and redistributed along the chromosomes, providing numerous variations. This means that the gametes produced by meiosis are varied in constitution, and some may develop into a new type of individual which has a better chance of survival than its predecessors.

The importance of variation has been neatly summarized by an American naturalist who said, "the versatile—not the meek—shall inherit the earth." Meiosis, with its vital phase of cross over between chromatids, is one of the main sources of variation in living things and only takes place in animals that reproduce sexually. Why is this quality of versatility so important? Are the advantages gained by reproducing sexually really so great that living things have found it worth their while to adopt this cumbersome process? The word reproduction gives an impression of an increase in numbers. At a cellular level the opposite is true. Fertilization interrupts the normal process of cell division and results in the formation of one cell from two, not vice versa. Similarly a bisexual population will not be able to reproduce at the same rate as a population of hermaphrodites or parthenogenetic females. With a bisexual population, the potential reproductive capacity is really limited to the female half, the males being so much "wasted" material. These all seem good reasons for managing without sexual reproduction. Many living things get round the difficulty by employing both methods, the more complex sexual method only being used occasionally, or when times are "hard."

Convenience is not everything. There are other vital factors to be taken into account. During the known period of the earth's history there have been great changes in the nature of its surface and in the sort of animals and plants that populate it. The prehistoric monsters that caught the imagination of such writers as Conan Doyle in *The Lost World* are not very far removed from present-day man in geological time. All living things have changed or developed to the forms known today. These changes have not been sudden and dramatic, but so gradual as to be almost imperceptible at the time, corresponding to the changing conditions in the earth's surface and atmosphere. Darwin worked out a theory related to these gradual changes which he called the theory of Natural Selection.

He felt it was necessary to explain why some forms succeeded at the expense of others and to define the forces which, he thought, were ceaselessly at work. Reproduction produces more individuals than can survive to reproduce themselves. They are said to struggle for existence. A codfish lays about four million eggs, only a few of which will reach maturity, and Darwin would say they had struggled for existence. The factors which weed them out are collectively called the forces of natural selection. But not all fertilized eggs are identical. Theoretically, in a completely inbred population, changes will take place in the structure of the chromosomes from time to time, this process being called mutation. In any ordinary population, mating at random, new variations will crop up due to the process of cross over during meiosis. There are infinitely more genetic patterns than individuals. These heritable variations, the changes brought about by mutation and meiosis, are the raw material for development in any species. Natural selection decides the direction of this development. It is in fact the force which causes one section of the population, rather than another, to have a disproportionately large share in the ancestry of future generations.

Suppose there were two families of rabbits, one white and one the ordinary brown. If they were taken to snow-covered country, natural selection might favor the white rabbits, because they would be less conspicuous to their enemies. In this case the brown rabbits would be eaten first and the white rabbits would contribute an increased percentage of young to the next generation.

The great changes that have taken place, such as the emergence of reptiles and from them the development of birds and animals, are called evolutionary. All evolutionary changes are ultimately due to changes in the gene frequency of a population. Gene frequency is a term used to describe the spread of a character through a population. Whether or not this character is subject to selective pressure depends on its various properties, on which chromosome it is found and so on. A recessive gene—that is, one which makes its presence felt only when present on both of a pair of chromosomes—will spread more quickly than a dominant one, since any detrimental effects it may produce will not be apparent at first. Not all changes in gene frequency have any evolutionary significance. It is therefore necessary to consider what factors may change these gene frequencies in a population.

First, the genetic nature of any population, except a completely isolated one, will be changed by immigration and emigration. As time has gone on this has been particularly true of humans. There has been more interbreeding between different populations and races in the last fifty years than in the whole of the rest of man's history put together. There are still a few isolated communities of men in the world which breed entirely among themselves, but their numbers are very limited and this produces different results from breeding in an infinitely large population, where mating is at random. Variations will tend to be constant in such a population. This means that the variations will cancel one another out under the normal laws of inheritance. But there is a contradiction in terms here. Random mating is not practicable in an infinitely large population, since the term implies that all males must have equal opportunities of mating with any one female, and this is unlikely. Even in these days of rapid travel, a man living in New York and one living in Chicago do not have the same chances of marrying a New York girl. They are all three members of the same breeding population and theoretically the two men's chances are equal. For all practical purposes, then, there are random fluctuations in the gene frequency of any population, because it is never truly random.

One of the most important factors influencing these random fluctuations is the size of the population involved. Changes can come about in the gene frequencies of small populations that would not be possible in larger communities; these changes have been named "drift." This drift can be described as the chance fixation, or loss, of genes of no adaptive value. Natural selection may account for individuals with useful characteristics surviving, but it cannot act on apparently useless ones. In a community where the men hunted at night, all those who inherited the ability to see in the dark would be at an advantage. If they handed this characteristic on to their children they also would be more successful hunters, and the character would spread through the population. It would be favored by natural selection. If the factor controlling the color of their eyes were due to other genes, these would have no adaptive value. Those with blue eyes would catch no more animals than those with brown. These characters would not be subject to natural selection, but might spread through the population by drift. An inbred population tends to become very uniform genetically, and once a gene is eliminated it can reoccur only by spontaneous mutation. It has been shown that sometimes a chromosome carries one of two genes at a given locus. The next chapter, dealing with sex determination, explains that some animals have two sorts of chromosomes, which are called sex chromosomes and autosomes. The details of their structure and distribution are of no importance at this point. It is sufficient to say that sex chromosomes are different in males and females. An example of a chromosome carrying one of two genes at a given locus is found in the sex chromosomes of tortoise-shell cats. Here the female has two similar sex chromosomes and is designated XX, while the male has dissimilar sex chromosomes and is called XY. Now fur color in these cats is controlled by two genes occupying the same place on the X sex chromosome: this gene may be for yellow or black fur and when a sex chromosome with the gene for yellow and one for black are present in the female (XX), a tortoise-shell cat results. Since the males (XY) have only one chromosome they will be black or yellow, but tortoise-shell toms do not as a rule exist. When two characters occupy the corresponding place on a chromosome like this they are called alleles. If two alleles, A and a, are found in a small population, it is a mere chance which becomes established at the other's expense. So changes can take place by chance in a small population which would be unlikely to happen by natural selection in a large one. Drift is a process which enables a change to take place from one genotype to another of greater "fitness," even though the intermediate types may be less fit than normal. "Fit" in this sense means well adapted or suited to the general living conditions. So the process of drift may well have been responsible for evolutionary changes in the actual nature of the chromosome, which could not have come about by natural selection.

Recurrent mutations will also alter the gene frequency of a population. A mutation by definition is a sudden change in the nature of a gene, which is then permanently handed on to any offspring. The rate at which a mutation spreads depends on a number of factors. It depends on how often the mutation crops up, the size of the population involved, and its rate of reproduction. In man only a small number of offspring are produced, but a larger proportion of these reach maturity and breed. This means that any non-lethal mutant stands a good chance of spreading through the population. Once a mutation begins to spread it will be subject to selection. For some reasons most mutants are disadvantageous in the homozygous state—that is, where they are found on both of a pair of chromosomes. Selection is usually between the heterozygote, where the mutant gene is present on one chromosome, and the wild type, where it is absent. The degree of selection will depend on which chromosome the mutant is located on. There are two types of chromosomes, the sex chromosomes and the autosomes. A recessive mutant on a sex chromosome will be eliminated before that on an autosome, since it will be apparent even when present on only one of the sex chromosomes. A recessive mutant on an autosome may spread for some time undetected, since it will appear only when present on both chromosomes of a pair, normally being masked by the dominant wild-type gene. A dominant mutant will be subject to the greatest selective pressure since it is apparent on all chromosomes. The spreading of mutant genes through a population is very important where evolution is concerned. Animals of different genotypes do not contribute offspring to succeeding generations in strict proportion to their numbers. Animals which contribute more than their share are said to be "fitter." This does not mean that they are best suited to their own surroundings, but that their offspring have a better chance of survival. Many mutant genes may make it harder to survive in one locality but very much easier in a neighboring one, and carriers of mutant genes may be able to colonize new areas to the general advantage of the species.

It all comes back to the fact that if a species is going to be able to cope with changing conditions, its members must have varying genetic characters. The importance of this variability is shown by a number of general developmental trends. For example, a number of animals and plants carry the male and female organs in one individual, but they nearly all go to great lengths to make self-fertilization as unlikely as possible. In man, both church and state do all they can to prevent breeding between very close relations. The church has a strict table of affinity, defining the forbidden relationships, and incest incurs heavy civil penalties. Why? There must be good reasons for these things. In all natural populations cross breeding seems to be vital if the species is to survive. Why should this be so?

First, there is the recurrent theme of the importance of variation. Genetic variation tends to decrease to a limit the longer a line is inbred. In fact for characters that are only slightly affected by outside conditions, inbreeding will lead to a genetically uniform population. Characters influenced by the environment behave differently. These characters appear more, rather than less, variable in an inbred individual, suggesting that inbred populations are less stable than outbred ones and more easily thrown off balance. Farmers and geneticists know that an inbred population may show a sharp decline in fertility and viability. This could be explained by the homozygotes for these characters being inferior to the heterozygotes. Natural selection acting on the heterozygotes will tend to produce a stable state in the population, but inbreeding will increase the number of homozygotes, and the fertility and viability will decrease. One of the reasons inbreeding so often has disastrous results in man is that it encourages the appearance of undesirable homozygous characters. Many of these involve some form of mental deficiency, and since they do not affect viability they are not eliminated. They may spread unnoticed in the heterozygous state, but with inbreeding the chances of their appearing as a homozygote are greatly increased. All the children from a marriage may inherit some undesirable recessive character, but if it is on only one of a pair of autosomes, they will appear normal. If these children marry people of very different ancestry the chances of these partners' also having the recessive characters are remote. If, however, they start to breed among themselves, a large proportion of their children will get the character from both parents and so develop the defect.

There is also a constructive aspect of outbreeding. An outbred population will contain a very varied collection of individuals from the genetical point of view. This means that a large number of genes will spread in the heterozygous state even if they have little adaptive value. If living conditions change, some of these genes may become a positive asset and they will be able to become established far faster since they are already widespread. In an inbred population they may reappear by mutation, but this is a slow business. An outbred population has a reservoir of genes on which it can draw to meet changing conditions. This ability to adapt to change is called evolutionary plasticity.

This begins to answer the question of why sexual reproduction is worth the extra trouble. Sexual reproduction is bound to increase the genetic variations in any population, through the processes of meiosis and fertilization. The advantages conferred by this variability are on the species as a whole, not necessarily on the individual. It is difficult to see how sexual reproduction could have evolved if the only advantages were long-term ones, enjoyed only by future generations. It seems probable that the process originated in single-celled animals and was passed on to their multicellular descendants.

What could have formed an intermediate stage between sexual and vegetative reproduction? It has already been suggested that recombination in bacteria shows something of the characteristics of both. It is also known in the Protozoa that sexual reproduction does not necessarily mean that the population is divisible into either males or females. There is a minute, ciliated, slipper-shaped protozoan, called Paramecium aurelia, where the individuals can be divided into one of two mating types. They are not distinguishable in the same way as the sexes of more complicated animals, but they will conjugate only with individuals of the opposite mating type. The genetic results of this process are very similar to the results of sexual reproduction in higher animals. The nucleus divides by meiosis to give two haploid nuclei; the two conjugants then lie close together and one nucleus from each passes across a bridge of cytoplasm to its partner. They fuse to form a diploid nucleus with a new set of characters. Maynard-Smith suggests that there is little difference between this procedure and what happens when one cell swallows another. Could the fertilization process in sexual reproduction have originated from cannibalism? If it did, some of the contents of the "victim" cell must have persisted and continued to function inside the "predator." For instance the chromosomes carrying the hereditary characters of the victim must have survived and been reproduced subsequently by the predator. In fertilization the sperms' chromosomes persist and contribute their material to the future embryo. It is worth recalling that viruses can carry over a single molecule from one bacterium to another, which is then reproduced in that bacterium and influences its characteristics.

The evolution of sexual reproduction to its present-day state must have taken place extremely gradually. It involves not only the fusion of two cells but also of their nuclei. This means that a meiotic reduction division must be included at some stage, or the number of chromosomes in the nucleus will just get larger and larger. A reduction division is not enough on its own. Pairing must also take place between homologous chromosomes before they separate and pass to the daughter nuclei. These are the details of the process. The vital step was the inclusion of chromosomal material from one individual in another and its subsequent reproduction. This may have come about by cannibal cells' having an advantage over their non-cannibal relatives and acquiring something akin to hybrid vigor.

From the point of view of the species rather than the individual, there are definite advantages in sexual reproduction. Fertilization interrupts the normal process of cell division, but this disadvantage is offset by increased variation and the adaptability that is acquired. Some animals and plants further overcome the disadvantages by reproducing vegetatively for the larger part of the time.

The chief drawbacks to sexual reproduction seem to lie in the difficulties of bringing mature gametes together, the vulnerability of the developing egg and the apparent wastefulness of the male. There are various ways round these difficulties. Some animals keep the differences between the sexes to a minimum, and the process of mating is somewhat haphazard. Others produce enormous numbers of fertilized eggs, only a few of which survive to maturity. Higher animals have developed complicated mating patterns which help to ensure that a few well-developed young survive to an age when they can themselves breed. Such is the case with man. Some animals and plants have abandoned all sexual processes and reverted to asexual methods. While they may flourish for a time, the development of a well-adapted community appears to be at the cost of losing future adaptability and decreases their ultimate chances of survival.

9

How Sex Is Determined

In ordinary human terms, who is responsible for the sex of the child? The mother or the father? Basically speaking, it is the father, although this answer rather oversimplifies the position. The last chapter explained how sex cells are produced by a "reduction division" called meiosis, and because of this they have only half the normal number of chromosomes. The human cell contains forty-six chromosomes—one pair of sex chromosomes and twenty-two pairs of autosomes, as the remainder are called. At the beginning of the century it was discovered that whole chromosomes controlled the sex of an animal and that these chromosomes behaved according to the laws of Mendelian inheritance.

In humans, the female has two similar sex chromosomes and is called homozygous, while the male is heterozygous, his sex chromosomes being different. As was mentioned in the last chapter, the female is designated XX and the male XY. The diagram shows that the sperm, formed by a meiotic division, may be X or Y, while the eggs are all X. The sex of a child therefore depends on the type of sperm provided by its father at fertilization. Theoretically X- and Y-bearing sperms are produced in equal numbers and the chances of any baby's being a boy are 50 : 50. In fact it seems that the two types of sperm do react differently to certain circumstances and the resultant embryos also differ in their viability, so that the sex ratio is not strictly 1 : 1. The chances of a boy at each fertilization are the same, however, and are uninfluenced by previous pregnancies.

This difference between the types of sperm leads to the question: can the sex of a child be chosen by the parents? As yet this is not possible, and if it is to be done the spermatozoa

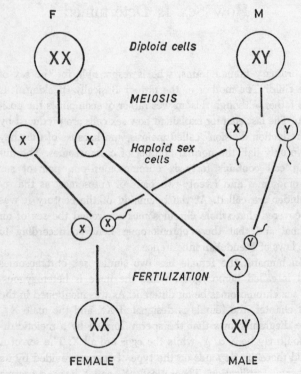

[10] *Determination of sex.*

must be treated before conception, since after that it is too late. The X- and Y-bearing spermatozoa of a rabbit have been separated by passing an electro current through the semen. When this semen was subsequently used for artificial insemination it was found that the X-bearing sperms had tended to move toward the positive terminal and the Y-bearing sperms to the negative terminal. If this type of technique can be perfected it will obviously be invaluable in agriculture, in eliminating unwanted bull calves from the breeding program of pedigree cattle. In humans it is possible that the same sort of results might be achieved by the use of chemicals on the seminal fluid. While this has not yet been managed, it is by no means impossible. Many scientists think the day is not far off when parents will be able to choose the sex of their children. It will be interesting to see what effect this has on the population. There are already millions of people quite incapable of making a simple decision. How will this vast army of "don't knows" react when faced with so important a choice?

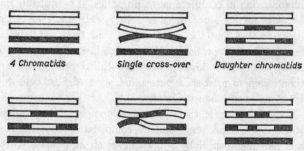

4 Chromatids   Single cross-over   Daughter chromatids

Subsequent division with another single cross-over

[11] *Hypothetical situation if crossing over occurred between sex chromosomes.*

Will there be a "fashionable" sex? In the animal world the ideal situation is that the sex ratio of males to females should be 1 : 1. Will this still be so if man has a choice in the matter? One of the drawbacks of increasing scientific knowledge is that it often brings increased responsibilities, but mankind's ability to accept its responsibilities does not necessarily increase at the same rate.

Incidentally, if sex chromosomes behaved in the same way

as the ordinary autosomes, the differences between them might be lost by crossing over. This is because during crossing over chromosomes pair and exchange portions, and after a time the X and Y might become so mixed that they would become virtually identical. In fact they pair over only a very short part of their total length, and crossing over between the sex portions, in this way, is made impossible.

Sex determination is not always a simple genetical process. When both the male and female sex organs are carried in one individual, animals are called hermaphrodites and plants are called monoecious, the snail and the sweet pea being common examples. Sex cannot be determined in these individuals in the same way as where only one set of sex organs is present. Practically nothing is known of the genetics of sex determination in complete hermaphrodites. It is probably not the same for all, since there is a very wide range of types. Some develop first the male organs and then the female; these are called protandric hermaphrodites. Others, where the female organs develop first, are called protogynic. Yet others seem to exist in a permanent state of flux, behaving first as males and then as females.

The intricacies of the sexual development of hermaphrodites are still a mystery. Equally complicated are those animals like the liver fluke and plants such as mosses, where sexual and asexual generations alternate. The mosses can be divided into two groups, the monoecious, which have both sets of sex organs in one plant, and the dioecious, where the sexes are separate. The monoecious mosses have an asexual phase and this produces a bisexual phase, where all the individuals have the potential for producing male and female gametes. This gamete production seems to be controlled by the nature of their environment and the conditions under which they develop. It is a far from stable system. What is more, in some species, such as Ectocarpus, the gametes themselves appear to vary in their potency.

It is necessary to distinguish between sex determination and sex differentiation. Sex determination is a matter settled right at the beginning of development. Sex differentiation goes on until maturity and is not always the expected expression of the animal's "genetical" sex. All the secondary sex organs depend for their development on the nature of the actual gonads—that is, the ovaries or testes. The genetic constitution of the parent is immaterial. The gonads release substances called sex hormones, and it is these hormones, not the sex chromosomes, which influence the development of accessory sexual organs. Sex hormones have been studied more in humans and the higher vertebrates than in any other group of animals. Their secretion is tied up with the presence of sex chromosomes in the cell nucleus, the nature of chromatin material in the nucleus during embryonic development influencing the formation of the gonads. Just because the sex chromosomes are of one type, it does not automatically follow that the secondary sex characters will be similar. It is extremely unlikely that an XX individual will develop a testis and therefore male sexual characters, but something may happen to upset the intermediate stage of hormone secretion.

Perhaps the most surprising of the characters to be so affected are the sex cells themselves. If sex is determined genetically the chromosome number of the sex cells might be expected to be important. In fact, the fate of the sex cells, whether they become ova or sperm, is decided not by their own genetic constitution but by differentiation during development. This comes about in the following way. The gonad can be divided into regions of different types of cells. In the females the cortex is highly developed and this region influences the development of ova. The development of sperm is influenced by the medulla region of the gonad, and this is the main region of the male's testis. The extent to which development is affected has been shown by grafting experiments on amphibians. Humphrey grafted some mesoderm, which would normally form the male gonad, over the future germ cells of a female Axolotl. Although these germ cells had female sex chromosomes they produced sperm. So the sexuality of the actual gametes is decided embryonically, that is during development, and not genetically.

This is apparent in other ways too. Farmers have known for a long time that if a cow has twin calves of different sexes, the female calf will be sterile, or what is called a freemartin. Dr. Lillie, of the University of Chicago, has done a great deal of research into the incidence of twinning in cattle, and his results have provided a great deal of general information on the relationship between hormones and the development of sex in early embryonic life. Dr. Lillie found that while twins developing in sheep had separate embryonic circulations, this was rarely the case with twins in cattle. Generally there was an exchange of dissolved materials between the cattle twins through the placental circulation. This is the temporary circulatory system which is set up between mother and fetus during development. Different animals have different numbers of layers of cells separating the two blood streams, and when these layers are few, more dissolved materials are likely to be exchanged. On further investigation he found some interesting facts and figures. Not all female calves born as one of twins with a bull calf are sterile. The percentage of normal female calves turned out to be identical with the percentage of twins that had entirely separate embryonic circulations. This led to the assumption that some substance was carried from the male embryo to the female, via the placenta, causing sterility. It then transpired that the testes developed, and were ready to secrete hormones, several days to weeks before the ovaries. The concentration of male hormones was sufficient to inhibit normal female growth and resulted in a sterile calf. Human twins, like twins in sheep, develop separately and are not influenced by either the mother's hormones or those of their twin.

It is now known that the ovary and testis are not the only organs to secrete sex hormones. These important substances are also secreted by the adrenal, thyroid and pituitary glands. It is difficult to imagine an elephant changing its sex, but less so if the animal is simpler and less highly developed. In fact the apparent stability of sex determination is affected by the time in embryonic development when it is first established. A chick, which is after all a fairly complex animal, can in fact effectively change its sex until about four hours after hatching. If a female chick is injected on hatching with the male hormone, testosterone, it will develop into a fully functional cock. Similarly, if newly born opossums are intercepted on their way to their mother's brood pouch and injected with hormones, they too can be made to change their sex. In humans and other placental mammals, the sexual organs begin to differentiate very early during development, often as long as seven months before birth. In these cases hormone injections at birth would be quite ineffectual.

So much for sex hormones and apparent changes of sex. What about the creatures that are neither male nor female? Little is known of the genetic constitution of hermaphrodites, and they are not the only intermediate sexual forms; there are also animals classified as intersexes. The simple theory that sex is determined by a pair of factors for which one sex is homozygous and the other heterozygous does not allow for the development of hermaphrodites, intersexes and cases of sex reversal. A more likely hypothesis seems to be that there are bisexual potentialities present, which are set in action or restrained by a controlling genetic mechanism.

At first sight the animal world appears to be divided into two clear-cut groups, males and females, but, as is already apparent, this is not the case. Besides the intersexes, which are truly intermediate types, there are also the peculiar forms called gynandromorphs. These are animals where different parts of the body have different genetic constitutions as regards sex. This has come about because of some abnormality during early cell divisions. These abnormalities sometimes crop up in the mechanism of chromosome separation during mitosis. If one of the sister halves of a chromosome fails to go to either pole during late mitosis, it will be left out of the daughter nuclei. This means that a patch of tissue will develop where the cell nuclei have fewer chromosomes than usual. If the eliminated chromosome is an X chromosome, the tissue developing without it will have male characteristics. For some reason these aberrations usually take place at one of the earlier segmental divisions. If it is actually the first division that is abnormal, the animal that finally develops will be half male and half female. Such abnormalities have been known in birds, mammals and insects. In fact among insects, parasitic wasps of the species Habrobracon have been found to develop with the head characteristics of one sex and the gonads of the other. Since sexual behavior in these insects is controlled by the nerve centers on the head, this must lead to an extremely frustrating sex life.

In scientific language, these gynandromorphs are genotypic mosaics—that is, their cells have different numbers or kinds of sex chromosomes. Intersexes are phenotypic mosaics but genetically uniform; this is to say their body form shows some male and some female characters, but genetically the constitution of the cell nuclei is the same throughout the body. Research on intersexes, found in the insect species Drosophila, has shown that some intersexes have an extra set of autosomes in the cell nucleus, or are triploid. This upsets the normal ratio between the sex chromosomes and the autosomes. Whereas in a normal animal the ratio is 2A : 2X, in a triploid intersex the ratio is 3A : 2X. This suggests that the autosomes carry some factor for maleness, since otherwise the ratio 3A : 2X would give not an intersex, but a female. It now seems probable that the vital factor is the ratio between the sex chromosomes and the autosomes and not the actual numbers of each present. As in so many aspects of genetical research, the fruit fly Drosophila has provided much of the information available on this subject of chromosome ratio. For example, part of the Y chromosome has been shown to be necessary for the fertility of the male Drosophila, but the whole is completely ineffectual during sex determination. Further evidence of the importance of the ratio between the autosomes and chromosomes has been demonstrated by the study of the different sexual types found in the fruit fly.

If animals can develop as hermaphrodites, intersexes and gynandromorphs, the fact that they can also change their sex does not seem so hard to accept. The external sex organs are so well developed in humans that it seems nearly impossible that a man should become a functional female, or vice versa. But a great many animals show very little difference between the sexes, and in some ways it seems strange that they always make the same type of sex cell, and that changes of sex are not more frequent. In actual fact many of the examples of sex reversal that are quoted are forms of hermaphroditism. If an animal develops one set of sex organs some time before the other, it is not always easy to decide whether it is a hermaphrodite or has changed its sex. Some even go so far as to have sex organs that develop and regress alternately. Some of the examples of sex reversal in humans that make the headlines in the more sensational newspapers are probably cases of intersexuality. In all cases of sex reversal the hereditary constitution of the animal remains unchanged. It is the outward expression of that constitution that varies.

One of the animals to show a regular change of sex is the hagfish. Hagfish are jawless, relatives of the lampreys, and are members of the only group of vertebrates known to change their sex regularly. They are hated by fishermen and have most unpleasant habits. They live on dead and dying fish, entering the soft tissues near the anus and eating everything except the outer skin and bones. They change their sex regularly from year to year, breeding one season as a male, the next as a female, and so on. They are not the only marine animals to show this unusual development; for some reason the edible oyster and the boring worm, Teredo, also alternate from one sex to the other. Some limpets who change their sex even go so far as to develop a penis which is reabsorbed when they enter their female phase.

Tapeworms show a somewhat different form of sex reversal, more akin to the hermaphroditism mentioned earlier. All the young segments of the worm are male. As the worm matures, the older segments, toward the back, become female and the last segments of all contain only ripe fertilized eggs, ready for shedding.

The type of sex reversal shown in birds and man is rather different. Birds are unusual in that they lay large yolky eggs, and there is room for only one ovary to develop. Usually the left ovary is functional and the right remains rudimentary. If the left ovary is destroyed, whether by accident or operation, the right ovary will start to develop, but what is somewhat unexpected is that it develops into a testis. The most likely explanation for this seems to be that "maleness" is suppressed by the normal development of the left ovary. When this is removed there is a change in the bird's hormonal balance and a shift to maleness. This influences the development of the undifferentiated gonad.

The cases of sex reversal in man follow no set pattern and a great deal of research is necessary before they are all explicable. All grades of sex reversal have been recorded, the most common being one where the male external genitalia are rudimentary, showing every gradation to the female type, while the internal gonads are male. These cases bear a marked resemblance to the freemartins in cattle. In fact the explanation may be very similar. It is known that during normal development the female hormones circulating in the maternal blood stream have no effect on the developing male fetus. They are unable to penetrate the placenta. If, due to some developmental accident, this barrier were removed or became ineffectual, then the female hormones acting on the developing male might well lead to intersexuality and an apparent change of sex.

When it was found that sex was determined in some animals by the presence of a special pair of chromosomes in the nucleus, this also explained why some characters seemed to be inherited by only one sex, such as color blindness and hemophilia. These characters are called sex-linked, and they have certain peculiarities. For instance, they may always skip a generation, or appear in only one sex. Another type of character, called sex-limited, also falls into this second category. These are characters caused by genes which can affect only one sex for physiological reasons. For example, there is a gene in the fruit fly, Drosophila, which affects the color of the testis sheath. This gene can make its presence felt only in the male, but it may also be present in the female.

The inheritance of sex-limited characters has been studied by agriculturists because sex-limited characters in cattle are very important to farmers, especially dairy farmers. The genes which control such vital factors as the gross yield of milk and the percentage of butter fat content are obviously apparent only in cows, but are also carried by bulls. When breeding dairy cattle it is easier to improve a herd by choosing a good bull, who can "serve" numerous cows, than to choose cows which will provide only a few progeny in their whole lifetime. The solution is to breed from bulls who have been progeny-tested—that is, bulls whose progeny have good milking records. These bulls will be about nine years old before their capabilities are proved. This calls for a farsighted agricultural policy. In spite of the disadvantages, this sort of breeding practice is not only possible but profitable. Denmark has long had a government program for testing and breeding dairy cattle and most of the first-class milk cows in Denmark are the progeny of two outstanding bulls.

Some characters appear sex-linked because the genes that

control them are located on the sex chromosomes themselves. When these genes are on the X chromosome, the pattern of inheritance will be criss-cross. If, for instance, the males of a species are XY, then the following result may be expected from crossing a homozygous female with a recessive character with a dominant male.

Parent	Homozygous Recessive Female	×	Dominant Male
1st generation	Dominant Females		Recessive Males

This means that in the next generation all the males are like their mother and the females resemble their father. This explains why it is called criss-cross inheritance. An example of this type of inheritance is found in the eye color of the fruit fly. A mutation is found in Drosophila which results in the flies' having white eyes instead of the normal red. This mutation has other effects and there is loss of pigmentation in other parts of the body. These include the colorless testis sheath already mentioned, when sex-limited genes were discussed. The gene causing white eyes is recessive to the normal red, and if a female homozygous for white eyes is mated with a red-eyed male, criss-cross inheritance will result. All the sons of the mating will have white eyes and the daughters red eyes. This can be represented in chart form by the following diagram, where Xw represents the recessive white eye color on the X chromosome and XW the normal dominant.

Parent	Females XwXw (white)	×	Males XWY (red)
1st generation	XWXw (red)		XwY (white)

One of the best-known sex-linked characters in man is hemophilia. This is a condition where the blood fails to clot, and leads to continual severe bruising and constant risk of hemorrhage. From the genetical point of view the gene that controls this condition is a sex-linked recessive one, generally apparent only in men and boys. It is transmitted by women from generation to generation. The diagram shows what could happen if a normal woman married a hemophilic man. Their daughters are all carriers of the disease and the sons are all normal. Daughter number one marries a normal man and has the chance of producing all four types of chil-

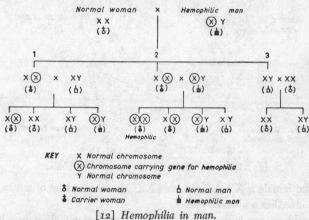

[12] *Hemophilia in man.*

dren. Fifty per cent of both boys and girls can be expected to be normal, while of the other fifty per cent the girls will be carriers and the boys hemophiliacs. Daughter number two marries a hemophilic man. In this exceptional case fifty per cent of the girls may be hemophiliacs, getting the gene from both parents, while the rest will be carriers. Of the boys, half will be hemophiliacs and the other half will be normal. The diagram also shows son number three married to a normal woman, when all the children could expect to be normal. If the son married a hemophilia carrier, then their family would be similar to that of daughter number one. This condition of hemophilia is due to a mutation. It is interesting historically in that it must have arisen either in Queen Victoria herself or in her parents, since she passed on the mutation to the ruling houses of Spain and Russia through her children, with disastrous results.

Hens, as will be seen from the diagram, have a different arrangement of their sex chromosomes from man. In hens

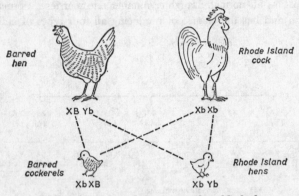

Barred hen

Rhode Island cock

XB Yb

Xb Xb

Barred cockerels   Xb XB

Rhode Island hens

Xb Yb

[13] *Color linkage helps to sex day-old chicks.*

the female is XY and the male XX. This is also true of moths, butterflies and some fish.

There are still some methods of sex determination which have not been mentioned and do not fit any of the patterns already described. The majority of animals have some genetical means of determining sex, either simply by a single pair of alleles or by a pair of sex chromosomes. Some mosses both have a genetical method and are influenced by their surroundings. But there are a few animals where the only deciding factor is the animal's surroundings. One of the best known of these is the marine worm Bonellia viridis. The male and female forms are so different that it was a long time before they were recognized as belonging to the same species. It is now known that if the larvae settle on their own, in an isolated place, they develop into females. If, during development, they come into contact with an adult female they become attached to her, in the most literal sense, and develop into males. The mechanism of the change is still being investigated but it seems possible that some secretions of the female stimulate the development of male organs.

Finally there is the method of sex determination used by the honeybee and others. Here the reproductive female seems to exercise more choice over the sex of her offspring than in any other known case. Sex is determined by the number of chromosomes found in the adult cell. The normal number of chromosomes found in a resting human cell is forty-eight—that is, twenty-four pairs—and this is called the diploid number. It has already been mentioned in connection with meiosis that sex cells contain half the normal number of chromosomes, in man twenty-four, and these nuclei are called haploid. In the bee all the females are diploid, or normal, but the males haploid. This gives the name haplo-diploid to this particular form of sex determination. What happens is this. The queen bee mates once in a lifetime. The sperms are then stored in special spermathecal chambers and she can release them, at will, to fertilize an egg. She lays these eggs continuously through her adult reproductive life.

Some eggs are never fertilized. Nonetheless they start developing and, because they are the products of a meiotic division, they are haploid. This means that they develop into males or drones. The eggs that are fertilized regain their diploid state and ultimately develop into females. Since the queen can control whether or not sperms are released for fertilization, she can also control the proportion of male and female eggs that develop. The developing females are affected to a large extent by their surroundings, which complicates matters still further. These fertilized diploid eggs develop into fertile females, future queens, only if laid in a large "queen cell" and fed on a high protein diet. The vast majority of fertilized eggs, laid in small cells, develop into sterile workers. This means that the queen produces three distinct types of bee, which ensures the continuity of a complex and highly organized community existence.

What is the likelihood of man's having this choice in the

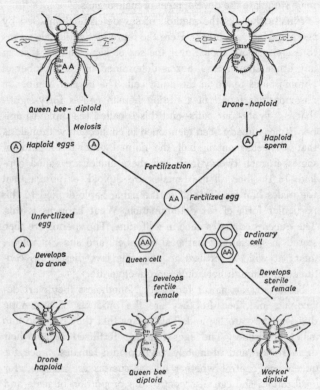

Queen bee - diploid

Meiosis

Haploid eggs Ⓐ

Ⓐ

Fertilization

Unfertilized egg

Ⓐ

Develops to drone

Drone - haploid

Ⓐ Haploid sperm

Ⓐ Ⓐ Fertilized egg

Queen cell

Develops fertile female

Ordinary cell

Develops sterile female

Drone haploid

Queen bee diploid

Worker diploid

[14] *Sex determination in the bee.*

future? It seems that it will be possible quite soon. The X- and Y-bearing sperms are, theoretically, produced in equal numbers and have equal chances of fertilizing the waiting egg. It is now thought that, in fact, the Y-bearing sperms effect a greater number of fertilizations than those carrying the X sex chromosome. On the other hand the embryos with XY sex chromosomes seem less viable during the early stages of embryonic life, and more XX eggs survive than XY. These two sets of circumstances seem to cancel one another out and the sex ratio remains half and half. It may be possible, in the future, to accentuate one or other of these tendencies and so influence the sex of the unborn child. Recent experiments have shown that hormones can have a great influence on the sex of an embryo during the early stages of development, modifying the sex already determined genetically. All these things form a sufficient basis for believing that a technical investigation, on a large scale, might find a way of treating the mother during pregnancy and determining the sex of the developing child. If such processes are found they will have to be applied with great forethought and wisdom.

10

Male and Female

Sex is often determined right at the beginning of a new individual's life. To human parents it can be something of great importance. But what are the differences between males and females? With human children the question is not an easy one to answer simply. Boys and girls are treated differently almost from birth: subjected to different influences, expected to have different interests, play different games and often to eat different food. This makes it difficult to be sure which differences are basic, genetical ones and which developmental; which due to nature, which to nurture. Not all animals even have separate sexes, and a great number of those that do show no outward differences. For years hyenas were assumed to be hermaphrodite because all animals appeared identical and were considered to carry both male and female sex organs.

Fundamentally the difference between males and females lies in the nature of their germ cells; among simpler animals this is the only difference. The gametes, or spermatozoa, produced by the male are always relatively small and have a tail or some other means of propulsion. They have a very limited life span once they are released from the gonad and therefore do not need to contain much in the way of reserve food supplies. Because they are so small they can be produced in large numbers, as many as two hundred and forty million in an emission, without putting much strain on the adult producing them, and many male animals produce large quantities of spermatozoa throughout their adult life.

The eggs or ova produced by females are very different, even in simple animals. There is a terrific range in the size of animal eggs, ranging from the microscopic human egg to that of an ostrich, which may hold over a gallon of fluid. The majority of eggs contain a relatively large amount of stored food, which is used by the embryo during development. The exception to this rule is the eggs of placental mammals which have to rely on their stored resources only for the few days before they become implanted in the mother's uterus and get their food from her. Apart from these, the amount of food stored in the egg is directly related to the length of time before the embryo is independent. The largest yolky eggs are laid by animals with the longest period of embryonic development.

In the simplest animals, living in the sea or fresh water, the differences between the sexes go no farther than the basic difference between the sex cells. These are liberated into the surrounding water, and need only the simplest of genital openings. Sometimes genital ducts are developed, and sometimes the gonads open directly to the exterior. To the casual observer the external appearance of the males and females is identical. Recognition is unimportant and they do not look after their offspring. Here sexual reproduction is in its simplest form and there is no need for differentiation between the sexes.

The differences between the two types of sex cell are fundamental and common to all animals. A great many of the sexual characters of vertebrates are connected with their emergence from water to dry land. As pointed out earlier, one of the chief problems facing early land animals was how to breed successfully. At first they returned to water to breed but later developed means of breeding on land. To do this the male had to have some means of placing sperm actually in the female's body, since sperm can only live in a fluid medium. This not only involved the development of suitable organs but also necessitated the co-operation of the female with all the attendant problems of recognition and the intricacies of courtship. The development of these characters led to a divergence in form and behavior between males and females. These characters are collectively called secondary sexual characters, since they are valueless if the animal in question does not have the primary sexual character of producing fertile sex cells.

These secondary sexual characters are generally concerned with size, body form and color. Sometimes the connection is extremely obscure but in many instances it is obviously essential to some phase of the animal's reproductive life, such as fighting or courtship. The massive antlers of stags are used for fighting and increasing the size of their harem, the brilliant feathers of the peacock's tail are used to attract and hold the peahen's attention. The type of character whose use is hard to see is the impressive mane of the lion, or the luxuriant growth of a man's beard.

The development of external genital organs obviously causes differences in the external body form of many animals, while in mammals the accessory sexual organs are conspicuous. The development of the mammary glands in the female and an external penis in the male at once makes the sex of the animal apparent. There are other less obvious modifications and while the value of some of these is easily explicable, in others it is harder to account for.

Archaeologists are able to tell the sex of human remains found during excavations, because of certain basic differences in the shape of the male and female skeletons. These differences are most marked in the regions of the pelvic and shoulder girdles. Men and women have an entirely different running and throwing action caused by differences in the arrangement of the bones in these two girdle regions. Female skulls are generally thinner and have a smaller cranial cavity, although men have yet to prove that they are of superior intelligence to women. The majority of women also have a higher rate of metabolism. Gynecologists use this fact occasionally in an attempt to forecast the sex of a child by counting its heartbeats before birth. If the rate is more than 130 beats per minute the chances are it will be a girl. The system is not foolproof, since it may be a boy with a fast pulse or a girl with a slow one! All these skeletal and metabolic differences help to explain the difference in athletic performance between men and women, and make it unlikely that they will ever compete in these spheres on truly equal terms.

These differences in form are not confined to humans. Cat fanciers can tell the sex of cats apart because of the heavy, bulging forehead of the tom, and pigeon fanciers can detect the slender and more streamlined head of the hen pigeon. With some of the crabs the differences are so pronounced that even an untrained observer cannot miss them. The claws of the female fiddler crab are the same size and quite unremarkable, but the male fiddler crab has one claw developed to vast proportions, forming the so-called "fiddle." The male salmon has a prominent hook on the lower jaw, although its function seems to be somewhat obscure.

Secondary sexual characters are very useful to the naturalist trying to identify one sex from the other in a particular species. It is doubtful whether the differences are always so apparent to the animals themselves. Some species of butterfly develop in a number of forms, or are polymorphic. Not only are the males and females different, but there are several different color types of female. This would seem to complicate the business of recognition rather than simplify it. Scientists now think that butterflies' eyes are far more sensitive to ultraviolet light than those of humans, and they are certainly most active during hours of bright sunlight. When these polymorphic forms are photographed in ultraviolet light they ap-

pear in patterns of blacks and grays. It is most probable that
the colors, as seen by man, are of no interest to other butterflies. They have no more significance than human hair color.

How have these characters evolved and what of the ones
that have no obvious function? Darwin gave this problem
some thought and, just as he had a theory of natural selection, so he also developed a theory of sexual selection. He
maintained that these secondary sexual characters evolved
for one of two reasons. They either enabled the animals that
had them to mate more frequently or to choose more fertile
mates. In Darwin's terminology a male is considered "fitter"
if he leaves more progeny than other males of his kind. For
example, in a polygamous species such as elk, seals or deer,
a male that fights and gets a large harem will leave more offspring than one that has only one or two wives. If his victory
is helped by horns, tusks, or some other secondary sexual
character, these may be inherited by the next generation and
so become established in the species as a whole.

In a monogamous species, where all mature individuals
have a chance to mate, the picture is more obscure. It may
be that, as in man, not all mature animals of any given species
do mate. Then those with well-developed secondary sexual
characters might be at an advantage. This theory has been
put forward by Lack in connection with the robin, where
investigation has proved that only about 80% of the population do, in fact, mate. Darwin had a different explanation. He
claimed that those animals with well-developed sexual characters who succeeded in mating also made "fitter" parents.
This is difficult to prove, since one must show that part of the
male's success is due to inherited characters and not just to
youth, good health and good luck.

Sexual characters may have evolved in some cases in connection with courtship and mating behavior. The different
plumage of male and female birds may help them to recognize one another. The male is often very aggressive during

the mating season and it may prevent his attacking and driving off a prospective mate. Some birds whose plumage is identical in the two sexes have developed elaborate recognition ceremonies. The development of these distinctive sexual characters also decreases the likelihood of mating with one of another closely related species. Mating between species usually results in infertile young, and the process is therefore of no advantage to the population as a whole. Secondary sexual characters in this connection serve as a kind of password; they enable animals to identify suitable mates of their own kind. On the whole, secondary sexual characters are developed by a process of elaboration and the resultant animals are a very far cry from the simplest animals, where the only difference between the sexes was the nature of the sex cells they produced.

One of the most widespread differences between the two sexes is that of size. The average man is taller and heavier than the average woman; bulls are far heavier than cows. Talking of bulls, a bull sea lion may weigh as much as seven times more than the average cow in his harem, an appreciable difference. Poultry raised for the table are another example of a male's having greater average size; stag turkeys usually come into the shops five or six pounds in weight heavier than hens, although reared under similar conditions.

Generally speaking, if there is a difference in size between the sexes the male is the larger. As with all generalizations there are plenty of exceptions which "prove the rule." One large group of animals where the male is smaller than the female is those who live in peculiar or hazardous surroundings, and where the male becomes permanently attached to the female's body, such as some deep-sea fish. These animals do away with many of the disadvantages of sexual reproduction. They do not have to find and court mates—they are always at hand. In many ways the pairs of animals resemble hermaphrodites, but they have the added advantage that the male and female still keep their separate identities and will produce variable offspring, not the uniform products of asexual reproduction.

If animals pair like that, it helps if one is smaller than the other. Why is the male always smaller in these cases? Earlier, while discussing male and female contributions to the fertilized egg, it was said that the female always made the major contribution of cytoplasm to the future embryo. The female sex cells are always relatively large and a far greater strain to produce. The human egg is only just visible to the naked eye but even so it is far larger than the spermatozoa. It is therefore logical, if reducing the size of one sex, that the male should be the smaller partner. His only significant function is to provide spermatozoa, and some males become so reduced in size that they are nothing more than a glorified gonad. This system would appear to have all the advantages of hermaphroditism and none of the disadvantages.

Animals that mate for life usually do so for a good reason. It may be that the actual process of mating is very hazardous or that mates are very hard to find. Animals such as man and some other mammals spend a large part of their lives caring for their young, and the pair stay together to share this work of rearing the offspring. It is noticeable, as far as man is concerned, that when some statistics on divorce were published a short while ago they showed a rapid increase in the divorce rate among the age group who had just finished bringing up their children, and among childless couples.

Some animals mate for life because they live in such peculiar situations that continually searching for a mate is quite impractical. One such animal is the burrowing shrimp, Callianassa affinis. This little marine animal lives in a U-shaped burrow through which it continuously forces a current of water. It depends on this water current for both food and oxygen. Its life is devoted to burrowing, and the work of maintenance and making extensions occupies all its time. If by chance it hits upon the burrow of an unmated shrimp of the opposite sex, they pair and remain for the rest of their lives, happily burrowing together. Otherwise it remains single. If the shrimps separated after one breeding season, they might never find another mate. These burrows are often shared with a pair of small fish, the blind gobies, who appear to mate in the same haphazard fashion and also remain together for life.

In a different sort of marine environment, angler fish also mate for life. The male goes to great lengths not to lose his mate once he has found her. These fish are widely distributed through the oceans, living near the sea bed at a variety of depths. For a long time only the females were known. These are distinctive fish which have a line and lure, like a fisherman's line, dangling a short distance in front of their unattractive mouths. This line attracts the small fish, on which the animal feeds, either by its movements or its luminescence. In either case their fate is the same. They are snapped up and eaten. The male angler fish is more wary and is unattracted by the lure. He seeks out the female and, ignoring her "bait," attaches himself to the skin of her head. His body then undergoes the most remarkable process of degeneration. His mouth, teeth, jaws, gills and fins all degenerate and the female's skin grows over him. When the process is complete he is enclosed in a sort of "wart." He gets his food from the female's blood supply and remains in this condition just waiting to fertilize her eggs. Once again these animals have the advantages of bisexual reproduction and hermaphroditism rolled into one.

This seems a somewhat undignified procedure, but at least part of the male angler fish remains outside the female's body. The male worm Bonellia does not retain even this small measure of independent existence. This worm has already been mentioned because of its strange method of sex determination. The female worm is a large sausage-shaped animal about four inches long. Half of this length is taken up by the elongated "neck," which has a food groove running along one side. The actual body contains a small sac where the eggs are stored. By way of contrast the male is only one sixteenth of an inch long and is covered in fine hairs called cilia. He uses these to swim into the egg storage sac and there he stays for the rest of his days. He attaches himself to the inner wall of this sac and gets all his nourishment through the female's body wall. In fact he lives a parasitic sort of life. The fascinating thing about these worms is the strange fact that males who fail to find females settle on their own and themselves develop into females.

The animals that have sharp differences between males and females also tend to have elaborate courtship patterns. The need for differences between males and females is accentuated by these patterns, which in their turn have developed as a defense mechanism. They help to prevent breeding between closely related species living in the same area; this problem is described more fully elsewhere.

In birds there is a terrific variation of form and color between males and females in some species, while in others the two sexes are identical in appearance. Many of the commonest British birds have very showy cocks and drab hens. The cock blackbird has striking glossy black plumage and yellow beak; the hen is a dark, undistinguished brown. The cock bullfinch has a lovely salmon-pink breast, black head and slate-blue back; the female is a very washed-out version of these colors. There are many more examples, but it is worth remembering that the duller colors of the female also serve a good purpose. While the male has bright, showy plumage which he uses in courtship displays, the quieter colors of the female allow her to incubate her eggs in greater safety and make her inconspicuous during the breeding season.

While there are only two sexes, male and female, plus hermaphrodites, some social insects have developed highly organized communities with rigid caste systems. Bees, one of the best-known of these social insects, have three main castes: fertile females or queens, sterile females or workers, and fertile males or drones. The queen develops certain distinguishing features that enable her to be picked out by the drones during swarming. One such feature may be the ability to give off a strong and distinctive odor. In bumblebees the differences are not so clear-cut. There seems to be a series of female types, ranging from the small sterile workers to the large females which will become the queens. It has been suggested that here there may be a connection between size and the degree of fertility.

The queen bee is a highly specialized egg-laying mechanism, and certain features set her apart from other inmates of the hive. The abdominal region containing the ovaries is considerably enlarged and this alone distinguishes her from the smaller, sterile workers. Her flight pattern is also very distinctive and her eyes are small. The males, on the other hand, have enlarged eyes, which they may need if they are to locate and fertilize the queen during swarming.

Ants have a similar sort of organization, but termites live in a more complex community. Ants, bees and wasps all live in a matriarchal society, where the males are smaller than any type of female and live as parasites merely tolerated for their value in the breeding season. Generally they are found in the nest for only short periods and in small numbers. The situation in termite nests is different. They make full use of all sources of labor and can modify or check the development of their young to suit the needs of the community. When the young larvae hatch they are indistinguishable one from another, and there are fertile and sterile members of both sexes. It is not yet known how this comes about, but sex is probably determined early in the egg and whether or not the eggs are fertile depends on the food supplies and surroundings during early development. There appear to be no fewer than sixteen different castes of termites, which may not all be found in one nest at any one time. The sterile castes make up the workers and soldiers. In some very highly specialized species there is a single egg-laying female, who undergoes a peculiar form of growth quite late in development. The back part of her body becomes enormously enlarged to contain the ovaries and she becomes immured with a male in a large mating cell. Mating takes place at intervals throughout life, replenishing her stock of sperms.

As mating behavior has become more complicated, so the differences between the sexes have become more pronounced. A number of factors have influenced the development of these differences. In man the differences seem to have gone beyond those of mere structure, and to affect the emotions and thought processes. The masculine and feminine approaches to life are basically quite different, a thing for which the human race may be grateful, since both are of great value and enrich ordinary day-to-day existence. If man were a uniform asexual species the world would be a very different place.

11

Breeding Seasons

The animals with which everyone is familiar can be broadly divided into two groups. The first, containing man himself and his domestic animals such as dogs, cats, cows and pigs, have no apparent breeding season and their young are not born at one particular time of year. The second group contains such familiar "wild" animals as foxes, deer, squirrels and a large number of birds. All these have a breeding season and produce their young in the spring. There are animals which come in the wrong group. Sheep are domesticated but have a breeding season, mice are "wild" but breed all year round. The fact that spring and summer are the seasons for plant breeding heightens the impression of productivity at these times. This is all true in our own temperate climate. What of the tropics, where only the coming of the rains breaks the monotony? Are the breeding activities of animals linked with their surroundings, or are they controlled by some internal mechanism?

Few animals are permanently ready to breed; even when independent of the seasons they show some cyclical rhythm, being more ready to breed at some times than others. The simplest animals, the protozoans, show a changing pattern in their sexual activity that seems akin to normal aging in more complicated animals. First there is a period of extreme vigor and they frequently divide by splitting in two. This shows them in their youthful virile prime. Next the cell changes, both chemically and physically, and individuals develop which mate by conjugation, or the fusing of two cells, and portray the more sedate characteristics of middle age. Lastly comes old age. The protozoa are no longer capable of any form of reproduction and eventually they die. The rate of fission in the first, or youthful, phase is affected both by the temperature of the surroundings and the amount of food available. Where protozoans breed both sexually and asexually, the sexual phase may be limited to the autumn when living conditions are generally harder. Although protozoa are sensitive to external conditions and influenced by them, they do not limit their breeding to any one season of the year.

When animals limit their breeding activities to one portion of the year, it is not always easy to see what has influenced their choice. There can be great variation within a single group of animals. Take the fish for example. A number of fish, in common with such shellfish as limpets, whelks and winkles, breed in the winter, a time when most animals do as little as possible. Many fresh-water and marine bony fish, as opposed to the ones with skeletons of cartilage, breed in the spring. Others, unable to find suitable breeding grounds near their winter quarters, migrate vast distances in order to provide their unborn young with the best possible surroundings in which to develop. The best-known of these migrants are the salmon and eel. Butterflies also migrate enormous distances, and edible crabs can be found journeying northward along the east coast of Britain.

Among the simpler animals, such as the jellyfish and its relations, the picture is complicated by the fact that they multiply both sexually and asexually. In many, asexual reproduction takes the form of budding. There is an oriental hydra which buds all through the winter until the beginning of the hot weather. The budding then stops and some hydras develop testes. The females seem to develop, if food is abundant, when a sharp rise in temperature follows a period of cooler weather. These animals are obviously very sensitive to their surroundings and the start of their breeding season depends almost entirely on external conditions. Most British sea anemones breed during the spring and summer; they lose this seasonal pattern if they are transferred to an aquarium where conditions are more or less uniform. This is not so surprising when one considers that the comb jellies in the Mediterranean breed all the year, there being little seasonal variation of climate. Their relatives, found in more northerly waters, have a very short breeding season, restricted to the summer months. The breeding seasons of many of the simpler animals do not appear to depend on some mystical internal mechanism. They seem to breed in response to certain sets of stimuli of a seasonal nature.

The cold-blooded frogs, toads, snakes and lizards that help to make up the great groups of animals known as amphibia and reptiles have very definite breeding seasons, because they are extremely sensitive to changes in their surroundings. This is only to be expected, since the very fact that they are cold-blooded means that their body temperature and general state of activity are very closely linked with the temperature of their environment. In cold weather they are very slow and sluggish in their movements, and in some cases are also dependent on seasonal water supplies in which to lay their eggs.

Even animals like birds and mammals, which are more or less independent of their environment, cling to their breeding seasons. Among mammals birth, not mating, appears to be geared to coincide with the easiest living conditions. Sometimes both happen more or less together, mating following almost immediately after giving birth. The internal rhythm of mammals seems to be strong and unrelated to seasonal changes. If animals are transferred from the Southern to the Northern Hemisphere it may be a couple of years before they adjust their breeding seasons to fit the seasons of their new home.

Mammals have various ways of ensuring that their young are born at a favorable time of year. There is a wide divergence in the length of time the embryo takes to develop in the mother. In rabbits, who have a short pregnancy of about thirty days, litters are produced from midwinter to midsummer. Other animals, with a longer pregnancy, mate in the autumn and well-developed young are born the following spring. Deer and sheep have pregnancies lasting about one hundred and fifty days, and with autumn mating the young are born the following spring, when the weather is warm and there is plenty to eat. Horses and asses prolong the embryonic period still further. Their pregnancies are eleven and nearly twelve months respectively and they mate almost immediately after foaling. Some animals manage to mate in the autumn and have their young in the spring with only a short period of embryonic development. In fact this is done in two different ways. Bats, for example, mate in the autumn and the sperm is stored till the following spring, when the female ovulates and fertilizes the egg with the stored sperm. Roe deer, on the other hand, mate in the autumn and the egg starts to develop in the normal way; when it has become a hollow ball of cells, and before it is implanted in the uterus, all development stops and it remains in this resting state for several months. Implantation finally takes place in December and the young are born the following May. Badgers, stoats and weasels also have this delayed development and although they mate in the late summer the young are not born till the following March.

All types of animals seem to have some sort of breeding season, since most tropical animals with no breeding season have relatives in more temperate regions that do have breeding seasons. Are they as clear-cut and well developed as those of plants? Since the majority of plants are literally rooted to the spot, they have to get their food from their immediate surroundings. This seems to make them more sensitive to general climatic changes than the majority of animals. Their breeding seasons are very closely linked with the weather, and all their reproductive efforts may be wiped out by some untimely and unseasonal change. Generally speaking, they show almost as much variation as animals in the ways their breeding seasons are determined. Those plants that have both sexual and asexual generations may only breed sexually when conditions are difficult, just as many animals do. There are some plants and animals which breed more or less continuously, and at the other end of the scale there are others whose breeding season is limited to only a few days in the course of a year. So many animals and plants seem to have their breeding seasons triggered off by changes in the climate and general surroundings that the question inevitably arises as to what happens to animals in a constant environment. The breeding seasons of birds living in the tropics are less well defined than those of their relatives in the temperate zones. What about animals living in caves and the depths of the sea? Here there are no seasonal changes. In the caves there is total impenetrable darkness, a very high degree of humidity and unvarying cold. Like the cold, dark depths of the sea, caves provide one of the most uninviting and monotonous environments inhabited by animals. In the twilight zones of the caves, conditions are more variable and provide a transitional area between the outside world and the caverns themselves. In most animals, breeding is restricted to certain times of the year when the necessary combination of stimuli are present. The surroundings of cave-dwelling animals are so constant that there is no reason why they should not breed all the year round, but sometimes there is just one factor that changes, and this is enough to initiate seasonal breeding.

For example, some Dalmatian caves are flooded every year, and some of the fresh-water animals living there confine all their active lives to this flood period, remaining dormant, in tough resistant capsules, all the rest of the year. Generally speaking, animals living in places like caves and ocean depths seem to develop breeding seasons only when their living conditions show some variation. This point is illustrated by the little blind cave shrimp, Niphargus. When it is kept in an aquarium it breeds during the winter, stopping when the temperature rises to 64°F. or above. Similarly in shallow wells, of less than forty-five feet, it breeds only in winter when the water is cold. In deeper wells, of sixty-five feet or more, the water temperature is unaffected by outside weather conditions and young shrimps are found all the year round. When conditions are more or less uniform, this animal has no set breeding season. It is not an inherited pattern but merely a response to external conditions.

In general, however, breeding seasons and sexual cycles seem to be affected by a number of factors. We may ask: Are these factors only such things as changes in the weather and seasons generally, or are there internal mechanisms which also affect reproductive behavior?

The simpler animals are generally very sensitive to changes in their surroundings, and with their very simple central nervous systems there seems to be very little internal regulation of breeding behavior. The more complicated animals are well aware of seasonal changes, but their nervous system is so developed that it also plays a part in changes in the reproductive organs, and some animals such as mammals would eventually come into breeding condition even if the usual external stimuli were entirely absent.

What are the factors linked with seasonal changes that are so important to breeding activities? One of the most important is undoubtedly light. At first it was thought that the quality of the light changed and this was the vital factor to which animals responded. It is now known that many animals react not to the change in light intensity but to the changing length of daylight hours. Ants come into breeding condition not only in the spring, when the days are getting longer, but also in the autumn, when the days are getting shorter. Birds are also extremely sensitive to changing light conditions. American juncos, which are a type of migrant crow, can adjust their breeding seasons to changing light conditions. Some experiments were conducted where two cages of birds were kept exposed to the weather throughout the winter. From October one cage had five minutes' extra daylight each day, the other cage had a constant day length. By the middle of November the testes of the birds in the first cage were increasing in size and by December these birds had larger gonads than those of birds arriving at their breeding grounds in the spring. The birds in this experiment seemed quite unaffected by the unusually low temperature.

Ferrets also respond to light changes, but they seem sensitive not so much to day length as to the contrast between night and day. Ferrets taken in midwinter, when their sex organs are normally undeveloped, were rapidly brought into breeding condition in the following way. The animals were divided into three groups, each subjected to different lengths of daylight. One lot had continual daylight, the next had sixteen hours of light in the twenty-four and the remaining group had the twenty-four-hour periods divided into alternate six-hour spells of light and darkness. Although this last batch were getting a total of only twelve hours' daylight, they were the first of the three to come into breeding condition. It is this fact that makes the contrast between night and day seem to be the vital factor. Other animals known to be affected by light range from field mice to turtles.

Some tropical animals react to light, which is strange since there is little seasonal variation. It seems that they are sensitive not to the day length or the contrast between night and day but to the ultraviolet component of sunlight. The breeding seasons of tropical birds coincide with periods of maximum ultraviolet intensity.

Daylight is not the only form of light that influences animal breeding. Some animals also appear to be sensitive to the moon and its changing phases. One of the most famous of these is a small segmented worm called the palolo worm. It is found in both the Pacific and Atlantic oceans. The Pacific variety spawn with such regularity at certain times of year that the natives of Samoa put to sea in anticipation of the event. The ripe worms are considered a great delicacy. All this takes place in November, a week after the full moon. At this time the rear halves of countless millions of worms back out from their burrows, break off and swim to the surface with a strange, corkscrewlike motion. At sunrise they contract violently, which releases the eggs and sperm, and fertilization takes place. The Atlantic species spawns a few days after the full moon in July, almost exactly a year after the previous spawning. The long-term timing is regulated by the water temperature but the conditions that influence the precise timing, confining spawning to the night of the first or third quarter of the July moon, are more obscure. It could be due to tides, but there seem to be a number of other factors involved. These animals may be in a transitional stage between an external and an internal regulating mechanism. The worms are mature before July and after this only two occasions fulfill all the necessary conditions for spawning. Only during the first and third quarters of the moon is the light intensity such that the sexually mature segments are attracted from their burrows.

There are animals whose cycle is completed annually, monthly or daily. The annual rhythm determines the period between each breeding season; animals with a monthly rhythm show a number of sexual cycles within each season and daily rhythms lead to breeding at certain states of the tide or when conditions are optimal. When all these three patterns are combined in the reproductive life of an individual animal, the breeding activities of that particular species will be extremely well synchronized and take place with great precision over a very limited period. Nor is the moon's effect confined to marine animals. Nocturnal animals such as bats and nightjars are also influenced by its phases.

Light is important to nearly all animals but there are also huge numbers who are unable to breed without water. Some animals, especially those in the tropics, have developed breeding seasons which are geared to coincide with the annual rains. This applies not only to animals, like frogs, that lay their eggs in water, but also to birds who need the increased food supplies brought by the rainy season.

There is a wood swallow in Western Australia which usually breeds in February and March, when there is a wet season. The rain does not always come in this part of the continent, and if there is a drought the birds will fail to breed until July and August when the second rains usually fall. Another Australian desert dweller is the frog, Chiroleptes platycephalus. These animals spend the greater part of the year buried in the ground in a state of suspended animation. When it finally rains they emerge in hordes and spawn almost immediately. The young develop very rapidly and are fully grown by the time the temporary water supply dries up. The precise way in which these animals react to the coming of the rain is not known but they are probably sensitive in some way to the presence of ponds and lakes, the degree of moisture in the atmosphere, or the increased food supply.

An adequate food supply is essential to the successful breeding of many animals. Birds breed from spring to autumn in response to the plentiful food supplies, but it has been shown by experiment that if sufficient food is provided all the year round, then the breeding season will be prolonged. Field mice in captivity have also been persuaded to breed continuously when there is plenty of food available.

Food, light and water must be present before most animals can breed, and must be there in quantity. At this time they

need more than the minimal quantity that ensures survival.
Cold-blooded animals and those living in the sea and fresh
water are also very sensitive to the temperature of their surroundings. The metabolism of such cold-blooded animals as
snakes and lizards is so slow at low temperatures that breeding is impossible; they do not even begin to move about freely
until the temperature rises. Some animals, like the cave
shrimp Niphargus, react in the opposite way. They fail to
breed when the temperature is more than 59°F.

The more complicated animals become, the less dependent
they are on the conditions of their surroundings. Cold-blooded
animals need outside warmth to give them energy to move.
Warm-blooded animals make the energy themselves by break-
ing down their foodstuffs and having an efficient blood circulation. Similarly with breeding; the desert frogs depend on
seasonal rain to provide ponds where they can lay their eggs.
Mammals provide a suitable place for their young to develop
inside the mothers' bodies. These more complicated animals
seem to have a complex internal mechanism which controls
the onset of the breeding season and the development of the
sexual organs, but this internal mechanism still needs to be set
in motion by some outside stimulus. This outside stimulus may
come from the animals' surroundings, such as longer days or
higher temperature, or it may be due to the courting activities
of the other members of the species. The two sets of factors
working together bring the animal into breeding condition.

What sort of internal mechanism is involved? Does it produce rhythmic changes in the condition of the sex organs
within a breeding season? Nearly all vertebrates are known to
have some sort of sexual cycle during their adult life, few
being in the condition to breed all the year round. Some,
such as the majority of female fish, come to maturity, shed
their eggs quickly and spend the rest of the year recovering
and building up fresh stocks. Typically the male is also ready
to mate only once a year. There are, of course, exceptions,
such as the dogfish, Scyllorhinus canicular, which is ready to

breed all the year round but shows signs of increased activity in the spring.

The frogs and toads have a slightly more complicated cycle, divided into three phases. They come out of hibernation and are ready to breed almost at once, spawning during the first fortnight in March. In April, when they have laid their eggs and sperm, their sex organs enter a period of great activity; this lasts till October and coincides with the animals' time of maximum feeding. At first any unused eggs and sperm are absorbed by the gonads, and this is followed by a rapid proliferation of new gametes in the sex organs. By October the animals are once more sexually mature, and there is a resting phase while they hibernate. When they emerge the following spring they are ready to start their cycle all over again.

Snakes, lizards and other reptiles have a similar annual pattern, but some male reptiles seem to be ready to mate all the year round and to have no definite breeding season.

These annual cycles are much the same as those of the simpler animals. Birds, and especially female birds, have a cycle within a cycle. The ovaries undergo rhythmic changes which result in the laying of an egg about once every twenty-four hours until the clutch is complete. This period of ovulation can be considerably prolonged if the eggs are removed as soon as they have been laid. An American bird called a flicker was persuaded in this way to lay seventy-one eggs in ninety-three days. The case of the domestic hen is a little different. Here the prolonged egg laying is due to a number of different factors, such as the plentiful supply of food all the year round, and to selective breeding.

These regular changes in the state of the ovary are even better developed in mammals than in birds, and are called estrous cycles. Some mammals have only one cycle during the breeding season and are called monestrus. Others have several successive cycles and are called polyestrus. The pattern and rhythm is most apparent in the breeding season of a polyestrus animal. On the whole the males tend to produce gametes over a longer period than the females, and the females therefore control the breeding season by their behavior and readiness to mate.

During the major part of the year the female is in a state of sexual inactivity, the ovaries are in a resting condition and there is no desire to mate. This is called the anestrus phase. It ends at the beginning of the breeding season and is followed by the pro-estrus period. It is during this time that the females come in heat or into season, due to changes taking place in the ovaries and associated organs. Each egg cell in the ovary is surrounded by a cluster of other cells, forming a structure called the follicle. These follicular cells help to feed the growing egg and also secrete hormones. When a female comes in heat, the follicle cells of the ovary grow rapidly and there are also changes in the uterus; this phase culminates in estrus when the animal ovulates. During both pro-estrus and estrus she is generally willing to mate and is receptive to any advances made by the male. If it is a fertile mating there is a period called gestation, while the embryo develops in the female's uterus, followed by birth and a time of milk production, or lactation. In some species the ovary has a resting phase after birth, in others there is another estrus phase, called post-partum estrus.

If mating does not take place, or is infertile, there is either a short recovery period, when the uterus and ovaries return to their resting state, or a pseudo-pregnancy when the changes that take place are similar to those during true pregnancy. All these events can be illustrated by a diagram of the sexual cycle of a mouse. These animals have an estrus cycle every five days, and in the unmated cycle a recovery period, called metestrus, is followed by a resting phase, called diestrus.

This diagram helps to explain why mice are able to increase their numbers with such astonishing rapidity. The cycle is further complicated by the female's having a post-partum estrus, or ovulation, immediately after giving birth to its

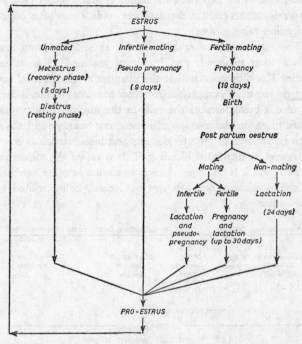

[15] *Sexual cycle of a mouse.*

young. If the mating is fertile, the ensuing pregnancy may be prolonged by as much as two days for every young one being suckled. This means the pregnancy may last thirty days, instead of the normal nineteen. It is, in fact, implantation of the new embryo that is delayed, the period of embryonic growth remaining the same.

The estrus cycles of other mammals differ from that of the mouse in a number of ways, but the same phases are usually present. Not all animals have a pseudo-pregnancy after an infertile mating, but in some other animals pseudo-pregnancy is part of the normal cycle, even when no mating has taken place. One other important difference is that animals such as squirrels, ferrets and the domestic cat ovulate only after copulation has taken place.

The estrus cycle of man and some apes differs from that of all other mammals and has been renamed a menstrual cycle. The difference is that the changes in the internal sex organs are more comprehensive than in other mammals and involve a breakdown of the cells in the uterus. In man, this takes place on the average of once every twenty-eight days. The breakdown of the uterine cells and blood vessels is characterized by menstrual bleeding. This is called the menstrual period, and it is not equivalent to ovulation in other animals. It comes midway between two ovulations, being related to the earlier one.

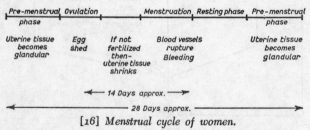

[16] *Menstrual cycle of women.*

In the premenstrual phase the tissue which lines the uterus thickens and its blood supply is increased. The wall of the uterus is then ready for implantation. This tissue is called the endometrium. The arteries that supply blood to the endometrium are of an unusual spiral type. If ovulation is not followed by fertilization, more changes take place in the form of the endometrium. It begins to shrink, due to loss of water, and the ends of the blood vessels are ruptured. The whole structure finally breaks down and is discharged into the cavity of the uterus, passing through the vagina to the exterior. Some of the factors affecting the menstrual cycle will be discussed later.

The sexual cycles of the more complicated animals are largely influenced by substances carried in the blood, called hormones. These hormones are chemicals produced by the ductless glands and some other organs. They have a specific and functional effect on other tissues and, as well as circulating in the blood, are also found to spread by diffusion. The key organ in the secretion of sex hormones is the pituitary gland. This is a stalked glandular mass found at the base of the brain. It is a composite structure and during development in the embryo is formed partly from ectoderm and partly from nervous tissue. In simple vertebrates, such as lampreys, the two component parts may remain separate, but in all higher vertebrates they are closely fused. It is nonetheless divided into the anterior and posterior lobes, which have different functions, and these regions may themselves be further subdivided. This complex gland secretes a variety of hormones, but those that have most effect on breeding behavior are secreted by the anterior lobe. The two principal effects of these sex hormones are to make the gonad's follicle cells grow, and to stimulate the gonads themselves to secrete secondary sex hormones. In the female these secondary hormones build up in the blood stream until they reach a point when they inhibit further activity on the part of the anterior pituitary. During estrus this concentration begins to fall, allowing the pituitary to become active once more. The two hormones secreted by the anterior lobe have cumbersome names, relating to their effects. They are called follicular stimulating hormone, or F.S.H., and interstitial cell stimulating hormone, or I.C.S.H.

One of the most noticeable effects of these hormones is that they are responsible for the maturation of the gonads and development of secondary sex characters, also stimulating accessory sexual organs. This becomes apparent when they are injected into castrated male animals, such as rats or cocks. Normally the gonads, or testes, do not start to mature until the first anterior pituitary hormones reach them. Then the I.C.S.H. stimulates the interstitial cells to produce a secondary hormone called androgen. This, with related hormones, is responsible for the development of such male characters as the growth of hair on the face and body and the changing timbre of the voice in man and the growth of the comb and wattles in cocks. The testis also secretes hormones called estrogens, usually associated with "femaleness." In fact the only difference between the hormones found in the two sexes is one of proportion. Both male and female hormones have a general stimulating effect, causing increased cell division and growth. The tissues of the sexual organs are more sensitive and, therefore, show greater response to stimulation of this kind.

The second pituitary hormone, F.S.H., has an important function in the process of reproduction in the female. In the ovary there has to be some means of releasing the egg into the body cavity. Each egg is enclosed in follicle cells with interstitial cells packed in between. The F.S.H. sets a train of events in motion which results in the follicle cells' becoming full of fluid and finally bursting, which sets the egg free. After bursting, the follicle cells re-form into a body called the corpus luteum which is important during pregnancy.

In females there is one additional hormone, progesterone, which both helps to prepare the uterus for a fertilized egg and stops the menstrual cycle during pregnancy.

The development of breeding seasons and sexual cycles is closely linked with the development of the anterior lobe of the pituitary gland. Its secretory activity is modified by nervous stimulation. A rabbit, for example, ovulates only after copulation, which provides the necessary stimulation to the central nervous system. If the connection between the pituitary and the brain is cut there is no ovulation, because there is no nervous stimulation. Similarly, in man, one of the commonest causes for the cessation of menstruation is a severe nervous shock.

The following chapter considers various aspects of sexual behavior, all of which are the result of a chain of processes. The anterior lobe of the pituitary gland becomes active and secretes hormones. These hormones cause the growth of the gonads, which secrete additional hormones. This results in a

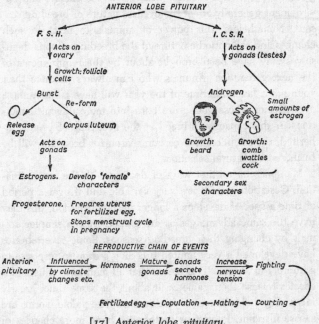

ANTERIOR LOBE PITUITARY

F. S. H.

Acts on ovary

Growth: follicle cells

Burst   Re-form

Release egg   *Corpus luteum*

Acts on gonads

Estrogens.   Develop "female" characters

Progesterone.   Prepares uterus for fertilized egg. Stops menstrual cycle in pregnancy

I. C. S. H.

Acts on gonads (testes)

Androgen   Small amounts of estrogen

Growth: beard   Growth: comb wattles cock

Secondary sex characters

REPRODUCTIVE CHAIN OF EVENTS

Anterior pituitary → Influenced by climate changes etc. → Hormones → Mature gonads → Gonads secrete hormones → Increase nervous tension → Fighting

Fertilized egg ← Copulation ← Mating ← Courting ←

[17] *Anterior lobe pituitary.*

steady increase in the nervous tension. This increased nervous tension in its turn leads to increased sexual drive, courting, mating and copulation. The vertebrate sexual cycle is divisible into three distinct parts. The anterior pituitary is stimulated by outside conditions, such as changes in the climate, through the nervous system. This leads to a secretion of hormones which brings about maturation of the gonads, and the further stimulation of the nervous system shows itself as sexual behavior.

These sexual cycles and breeding seasons are a complex series of processes. How have they developed? Do they save a wastage of eggs and sperm? Do they help a species to have greater reproductive success? Changes in the climate and environment generally affect the cyclical nature of breeding seasons. Nonetheless, this power of animals to react to such changes and the periodic nature of the breeding seasons themselves may have been brought about by the requirements of the next generation. Animals who can always produce their young at a favorable time of the year will have an advantage over species whose young are born into more difficult conditions. If this capacity to breed at the best time of year is inherited, the adoption of a certain season for breeding will be furthered by natural selection.

Mammals have other ways of dealing with the same situation. Gestation periods are very variable and if over a period of time a species develops a longer gestation period, this may have the same advantages as are gained by the simpler animals by changing their breeding seasons. Some invertebrates have developed a very limited breeding season in response to a number of stimuli. This means that all mature members of a species release their gametes at about the same time, greatly increasing their chances of fertilization. The palolo worms are a case in point. Polyestrus vertebrates have more chances of achieving reproductive success—that is, a fertile mating—than monestrus animals, since there are a number of heat periods in each breeding season.

The production of gametes, and particularly of large yolky eggs, is a severe physiological strain on any animal. It is therefore an advantage if the period of sexual activity, when these eggs are produced, is limited in some way. Breeding seasons do just this and, by also concentrating the production of young into the best months of the year, increase their chances of survival and benefit the species as a whole.

The elaborate processes of sexual reproduction are mostly the direct, or indirect, result of the need to bring the ova and sperm into contact with one another as quickly as possible after their release from the gonads. Some animals produce mature gametes all their lives, so that fertile mating is always possible. This is wasteful and rare. Another method is that the gametes may only be released in response to external stimuli which affect both male and female. Finally, mature gametes may only be produced in response to internal stimuli. Male apes and man are among the few animals that produce mature gametes continuously. The vast majority of animals produce their gametes in response to external stimuli, and these animals have well-defined breeding seasons. Female mammals use the third method and produce ova in response to internal stimuli, the menstrual cycle proceeding quite independently of external conditions.

The situation in man is quite unique. The male produces gametes continuously and the female has a monthly cycle which is quite independent of her surroundings. This means that sexual desire and the drives arising from sexual impulses are no longer connected with reproduction. Since man is also unique for the development of constructive and logical thought impulses, it would be interesting to know whether these two things are linked and if so how. Which came first, the separation of sex and reproduction or the development of the human mind? Whatever the answer, this situation has brought its own crop of complications which are, as yet, far from solution.

12

Fighting and Territory

Fighting among animals is a commonplace occurrence and falls under one of two broad headings: fighting for survival and fighting for sex. Of the two the latter is by far the more common. There is all the difference in the world between the ghastly noise made by two fighting tom cats and the agonized screams of a rabbit fleeing from a weasel. The cats are two of a kind fighting for a particular reason; on another occasion they may pass each other without a second glance. The rabbit and the weasel are the hunted and the hunter, both intent on survival, one looking for food, the other to save its life.

Reproductive fighting is the only concern of this chapter. All types of vertebrates engage in this sort of contest. It is less widespread among invertebrates. This is not really surprising. Animals must be able to co-ordinate their movements before they can fight, and this presupposes a well-developed central nervous system. Animals like jellyfish, which drift about at the mercy of ocean currents, obviously lack the equipment necessary for fighting. The invertebrates which do fight are such animals as spiders, insects and octopi; they are nimble and obviously have an efficient nervous system.

Not all animal fighting consists of spectacular battles. It depends upon what weapons are available. Male butterflies, competing for the attentions of a female, buffet each other with their wings. As is so often the case, the female is a passive and apparently disinterested spectator, willing to accept as a suitor whichever male is the winner. This is not a very desperate affair compared with the struggles of two wild rams. They stand some feet apart, heads lowered, and then charge, meeting in a shattering head-on collision. The impact can easily have fatal results, either through fractured skulls or through one of the ram's being pushed off one of the narrow mountain ledges. Occasionally the battles are brief and no damage is done. Other animals without any obvious weapons make use of such things as teeth and hoofs. Dogs, cats, fish and even seagulls bite one another viciously, and horses lash out with their hoofs. Even rabbits and hares have battles, rearing up on their hind legs, boxing with their forepaws and biting and squealing the whole time.

But not all fighting is so ferocious, and very few are battles to the death. There is no such thing as a consciously brave animal and no shame in running away so that they may fight another day. Much of the fighting that goes on is nothing more or less than an elaborate bluff. The victor is not the stronger, but the one able to put on the greater show of ferocity and so intimidate his opponent.

This is where territory comes into the picture. Competitive fighting serves a useful purpose only if kept within reasonable limits. It becomes pointless if so many males are killed or wounded that the breeding stock is seriously depleted. If the males spend all their time fighting, then it will be at the expense of other activities. It is a great waste of effort if fights begin between animals who are competing for neither breeding grounds nor mates. This danger seems to be avoided by animals' being roused only by their rivals. Others, noncompetitors, leave them cold.

When an animal is defending its territory it will become aggressive only in certain surroundings. If a man meets a chance acquaintance in the street he will probably smile or say "good morning." If he meets the same man wandering, uninvited, round his house or garden, his attitude is likely to be aggressive. Tinbergen has designed some experiments with sticklebacks that bear this out. He placed two male sticklebacks in a large aquarium and gave each of them time to establish a territory. Then he caught them and put them in separate wide glass tubes. When the two tubes were lowered into A's territory in the aquarium, A tried to launch a violent attack on B through two thicknesses of glass; B tried frantically to escape. When the two tubes were lowered into B's territory the situation was immediately reversed, and B tried to attack A. When they were living undisturbed in the aquarium neither ventured into the other's ground. Very little is known about how animals learn to recognize their own territory. They seem to orient themselves on certain objects and to become used to definite landmarks. Occasionally visible landmarks are of only secondary importance. There is a little fish called a bitterling which lays its eggs in a mussel shell. These fish show only a very slight reaction to the sight of a mussel shell; what does interest them is the water in which a live mussel has been kept. If this water is bubbled through an empty shell they show a very definite response. In this case they seem to identify the mussel by some chemical it gives off and the current of water that it sends out.

Bluff also limits fighting. Many animals have developed conspicuous characteristics which they use to intimidate their rivals. Color and plumage are often strikingly well developed by male birds and are very effectively displayed when they adopt threatening attitudes. It is at this time that the peacock's tail is seen to best effect, as are the striking black, gold and red feathers of the cock goldfinch. Not all animals rely on brilliant colors; sometimes it is noise that intimidates. The vocal sacs of the male gorilla are far larger and better developed than those of the female and he can make a really deafening noise. Smell is also used to warn off rivals. Dogs urinate and brown bears rub up and down trees, also urinating, as a warning to other males in the area that they are in a fighting mood.

The warning signals serve the same purpose as the actual fighting itself, spreading out the males. This reduces the likelihood of their all trying to mate with the same female while a number of other females remain unmated.

The staking of territory also serves other purposes. It spaces out the breeding animals and helps to avoid overcrowding. An overcrowded breeding site has several drawbacks: it presents a large target to a marauding enemy and may lead to lack of food and the rapid spread of disease. It is a pity that this instinct for spacing breeding sites has vanished in man with the spread of so-called civilization. The human slum has no equivalent in the animal kingdom.

Sometimes the animal's purpose in defending its territory is obvious; at other times the reason is more obscure. It is easy to see why birds guard the part of their territory that holds the nest and why some males guard their mates. Sometimes it is very apparent that the male is defending neither the nest nor his mate. Perhaps in this case the territory provides an emergency larder. This is particularly important for birds incubating eggs. It means that food is readily available and that the eggs need be left for only very short spells, which lessens the risk of their getting cold.

Animals that have a communal life often fight over food and sleeping places, as well as for the right to breed. In these groups the amount of actual fighting is often reduced by learning. An animal learns which members of the group are stronger, and therefore to be avoided, and which can easily be intimidated. Each animal can find its place in the group and an order of dominance, or pecking order, is established. These orders are found in many groups of social animals, such as chimpanzees, birds, fish and, most particularly, domestic hens. Birds living in a hen run seem to have two separate rankings for dominance, one for cocks and one for hens. The number one hen can feed freely and usually lays most eggs. She is not necessarily the hen that is most frequently mated by the cocks. A lower-ranking hen may hold this position, and while she lays fewer eggs, a far higher percentage will be fertile. A hen's place in the pecking order will depend on the general condition of her reproductive organs. If a hen at the bottom of the order is injected with extracts of male hormones, she becomes very belligerent and will rise to number one. When the injections stop she will revert to her former position at the bottom of the ladder. If these animals, or others, are confined in cages or a very limited run, the importance of the pecking order becomes exaggerated and develops into a pecking right. The general development of social dominance is probably an adaptation to living in rather restricted or overcrowded conditions. It enables members of a group to coexist peacefully and get their food without wasting a lot of energy on disputes and fighting. The following lines by Cowper sum up the whole situation, putting both fighting and timidity in their proper perspective. He wrote:

> To combat may be glorious and success
> Perhaps may crown us, but to fly is safe.

Is size a significant feature in display and fighting? When matings are uncontested a female will mate as willingly with a small mate who courts her as a larger one, so that size is very rarely an inherited characteristic. We do find, however, that some animals have one or more organs disproportionately developed and use these organs both in threat displays and battles. The stag beetle was given its name because of the huge antlerlike spikes on its head. Unlike the antlers of deer, these are actually projections of the jaw. They are greater in the male than in the female and reach their maximum size in those adults which have had plenty to eat during the larval stage of their life history. They use these antlers in their mating battles. When two males come to grips, each tries to turn the other on his back by prodding with his antler. If one beetle is unlucky and is thrown on his back, he lies there helplessly waving his legs in the air while his opponent makes off with the female. The antlers and horns of some of the hoofed animals are similarly characters that have become excessively developed and are also used in mating battles.

Not all animals need great size to make their threats effective. Many, like the lion, simulate it. They manage to make themselves look far larger when they are roused. Dogs raise their hackles, birds fluff out their feathers and spread their wings and some fish can blow themselves up like footballs. These displays warn intruders that they are trespassing, and seem to be remarkably effective. Where the animals go further than threats and actually come to blows, size may be the deciding factor in an encounter. Just as a heavyweight boxer will have little trouble knocking out a bantamweight, so the larger and heavier animal will usually win. But excessive development of such things as antlers is not always an advantage and can be carried too far. The weight of the horns of a bull elk, expressed as percentage of his total weight, rarely reaches more than 3%. Dr G. G. Simpson has investigated the prehistoric Irish elk. This seems to have had some simply massive antlers. The problem of how to balance this weight must have been complex. It is quite a strain to balance a heavy book on one's head, but the antlers of the Irish elk were sometimes as much as 10% of the total body weight. The muscles needed to keep the animal's head upright must have been massive, and after the antlers had been shed their annual replacement must have been a great strain on the animal's strength. Such an inordinate increase in size seems to have been more of a disadvantage than an advantage in the long run, and could have contributed to the extinction of the species.

Many sea birds have no problems in finding food for their young, but extreme difficulty in getting a suitable breeding site. They have, therefore, well-developed threat displays, with which they try to maintain their claims. It is vital for colonial birds to claim sufficient territory to ensure privacy. Otherwise they will be constantly attacked by others in the colony, especially while copulating. A variety of birds are enraged by the sight of others of their species mating and will make repeated attempts to interfere. Various species of gulls become hostile when they see companions engaged in the food begging and courtship feeding that form the normal prelude to copulation. The sexual acts of others also arouse antagonism in both apes and man, though in man the primitive hostility is often rationalized on moral grounds. The behavior of Eskimo dogs serves to illustrate the close connection between sex and territory. Immature dogs do not hold territory of their own and seem oblivious to the territorial claims of others. As soon as they are sexually mature their attitude changes. Within a week of their first copulation they establish their own territory and avoid that of other dogs.

Whether or not animals will fight depends ultimately on the level of sex hormones in their blood and their general reproductive condition. Immature animals and those whose sex organs are underdeveloped are seldom involved in fights. The signals which cause one male to attack another vary, but generally give some indication of the contestants' maleness. A male robin will fly toward the sound of another's song, but will not attack until he sees the singer's red breast feathers. Tinbergen says that trespassers suffer from bad conscience and defenders are full of righteous indignation. Signs of maleness intimidate the trespasser and enrage the defender.

The focal point of the territory varies from species to species. The nest site is often the vital spot for colonial birds and is connected both with copulation and rearing the young. This is not always the case. There is a species of Australian magpie which lives in groups, and both breeding and nonbreeding birds defend this communal territory against those outside the group. Sexual relations among the group are entirely promiscuous and the female builds the nest and rears the young on her own, the male showing absolutely no interest.

The American sage grouse and prairie chicken organize their lives differently, combining some of the advantages of both these systems. Sage grouse establish both territorial claims and a pecking order which reduces fighting to a minimum. This also means that the most virile males achieve the highest number of matings. Their mating arenas are an impressive sight. They can be half a mile long by two hundred yards wide and may contain as many as four hundred males. These males display and spar for two or three weeks, fighting by beating their wings and pecking. In this way they establish both a territory and an order of dominance. When the females arrive they congregate in groups in little areas twelve or fifteen feet square. These groups are guarded by a master cock, a sub cock and up to six guard cocks. The mating privileges of these birds are regulated by their place in the hierarchy. The master cock struts around, head thrown back and wings spread. He makes a curious "plop" sound, too, by deflating his air sacs. The females adopt a submissive attitude, inviting mating, and the master cock may mate with twenty or more hen birds in a morning. Sometimes, due to satiety or a slackening of his sexual drive, a master cock ignores a soliciting hen; then the sub cock steps in and mates with her. The guard cocks get a chance to mate only if the sub cock also appears uninterested. When the territories are indefinite or unusually crowded, mating birds are subject to a great deal of interference from neighboring cocks. Generally speaking, it is a highly organized system, allowing the most virile birds the greatest chance of breeding. In fact, these species seem to have reached a compromise between social integration and breeding exclusiveness.

These are the advantages in having a territory for a colonial bird. What about non-colonial birds? It is as important for a robin or a wren to breed without fear of interference and interruption as it is for a gull or a penguin. These less gregarious birds still base their territories round the nesting site and may have to defend both site and nesting material from the depredations of their rivals. The territory is also important as a larder, but the impulses that cause an animal to defend its territory seem more closely connected with sex than with hunger.

Generally speaking, animals seem to have developed patterns of behavior that reduce fighting, but there are still those who fight with the sole object of rendering their opponents sexually impotent. Squirrels and other rodents fight very fiercely and as they roll about on the ground they squeal and struggle to castrate one another. Apart from fighting to the death, there is after all no other method so effective for reducing the numbers of one's reproductive rivals. In fact these animals can withdraw their testes to safety in the body cavity, but sometimes they forget in the excitement of the fight and emasculated rodents are not uncommon. Nor is this destruction of reproductive rivals limited to males. When the queen honeybee emerges, the very first thing she does is destroy the contents of all other queen cells, leaving herself an undisputed field for her breeding activities.

Fighting demands a high degree of nervous co-ordination. Limbs, eyes and brain must all work quickly and together; which means that fighting is confined to the more complex animals. The most advanced animals have developed elaborate songs, dances, colors and behavioral patterns, so that they can both warn and threaten their rivals without actually coming to blows. Those that have made most progress have abandoned fighting and can put their energies to better use.

13

Development of the Egg

No one knows for certain how life began, although there are various well-argued theories. The life of a new individual begins during reproduction and is an astonishing process. If the starting point for the story of development is taken as the time of fertilization, it should be remembered that many complex processes must already have taken place to make the fusion of egg and sperm possible. The two types of cell that come together to form the egg are among the most complex in the body. The fertilized egg contains the inheritance of both maternal and paternal lines. It also carries enough nourishment to last the developing embryo until it is able to fend for itself. Eggs may be minute; they may be enormous. They may have complicated colored or sculptured shells, enabling their species to be recognized at a glance; they may have no shell at all. They may be laid at random in the vastness of the ocean; they may develop inside the mother, emerging as an independent individual. The human egg contains very little yolk and is about 0.1–0.2 mm in diameter; an ostrich egg contains large quantities of yolk and its diameter is about 85 mm. Even the quantities of eggs produced vary; a whale produces one egg every two years, a codfish lays six million eggs in one breeding season. Yet all of these are eggs and responsible for the continuance of the species.

The word egg tends to conjure up a picture of a hen's egg, since that is the one most commonly seen. But a hen's egg is a composite structure. It is only the yolk which forms the ovum or true egg, and is comparable to the simpler eggs of a worm or a sea anemone. The "white" and the shell are different types of egg membrane. These membranes are secreted, by various glands in the reproductive tract, as the ovum makes its way from the ovaries to the outside world. The jelly round a frog's egg is a similar secretion to egg white and both substances are technically called tertiary membranes. Some shells are horny, like the mermaid's purse of dogfish; others leathery, like the eggs of the quaint Australian duck-billed platypus. The development of these egg membranes has been one of the most important steps in the animals' colonization of land.

The ocean contains all the salts and water any developing egg could need, and marine fish do not have to make any special provision for their young. The codfish's egg contains no water and only a droplet of oil. This is sufficient to feed the embryo until it is ready to hatch. Frogs and toads and other amphibians include some water, their eggs being comparatively large and complicated. The first animals to manage to live on land were reptile-like, and the reptiles enclose their eggs in a shell, which means they can hold enough water to last them throughout their development. The process is incomplete in the turtles and their eggs absorb some moisture from the damp sand in which they are laid. Birds have completely solved this problem and even water-birds' eggs are independent of their surroundings. While the complete enclosure of the eggs in shell membranes means that they can be laid anywhere, irrespective of water supplies, there is then no way for the embryo to get rid of waste matter. The invertebrates excrete most of their waste products as ammonia, which is very diffusible and soon disappears in the surrounding water. Fish excrete their nitrogenous waste as a chemical compound called urea, which is both less poisonous and less soluble than ammonia. The embryos of land animals excrete uric acid, which is very insoluble. In mammals the excretory products do not have to be stored in a closed, boxlike egg. They excrete urea, which passes through the placenta and into the maternal circulation.

So much for the general structure of eggs and ova. The primary function of the ovary is to provide these ova ready for fertilization. As animals have developed there has been a tendency to increase egg size and reduce the number of eggs produced. Eggs with a small amount of yolk usually develop quickly, either hatching into an intermediate form called a larva or into a simple adult. Those with a lot of yolk develop more slowly and often hatch as a more complex individual. In birds' eggs, where the yolk is supplemented by albumen, or white, the larval stages are cut out altogether and the young hatch with all their adult characters.

The ovaries of birds and mammals not only produce ova but also function as endocrine organs, secreting sex hormones. This is particularly important in mammals, where the uterus has to be ready to receive the eggs shortly after fertilization. The changes in the uterus are associated with the heat periods and in humans are shown by the monthly menstrual cycle. What use is this menstrual period? Most mammals only produce eggs intermittently and the uterus is prepared for them, since if this were not so the eggs might be wasted. When the eggs and the uterus are ready, the behavior of the female changes and she is in estrus, or in heat. It is at these times she is most ready and willing to receive a mate. Menstruation in humans is not, as is so often supposed, the equivalent of the heat period of other mammals. The equivalent time in man falls midway between two menstrual periods. Humans are unique, however, in that the females' sexual activity is not confined to the time of ovulation as in other animals, but may take place at any time between menstrual periods. While many male animals are able and willing to mate all the year round, they generally need the stimulus of a mature and receptive female. It is claimed that the only two kinds of animals to perpetrate rape are white mice and man. No other animal will attempt sexual union if the female shows herself to be entirely unco-operative, since, from the viewpoint of the species as a whole, infertile matings are a waste of time and energy.

Fertilization is the beginning of a new individual, development starting the moment the nuclei from the parents' sex cells fuse. A great deal of preparation is necessary before this is possible, since both male and female sex cells must undergo a process of maturation before they are ready for fertilization. These maturation divisions, described in an earlier chapter, halve the number of chromosomes carried in the nuclei of the sex cells, the normal number being restored during the fusion process of fertilization.

There are two meiotic divisions fairly early in the development of the spermatocyte, with only a short interval between, so each spermatocyte gives rise to four sperms. Sperms are usually more or less uniform in structure irrespective of the animal that produces them. The head contains the sperm nucleus, the middle portion contains one or more centrosomes and there is a tail. This tail gives the sperm its mobility, which is one of the diagnostic features of a male gamete.

The maturation of the ovum is rather different and contributes far more material than the sperm to the fertilized egg. The main structures of the embryo are formed from the cytoplasm of the egg, which must also provide the food reserves for the development. There is usually a long period of growth which interrupts the continuity of the maturation divisions. In some invertebrates maturation divisions are not resumed until stimulated by fertilization; most vertebrates complete the first maturation division and the second follows fertilization. These divisions are very unequal; the small cell produced at the first division is called the first polar body, and at the second division it divides again; the ultimate products

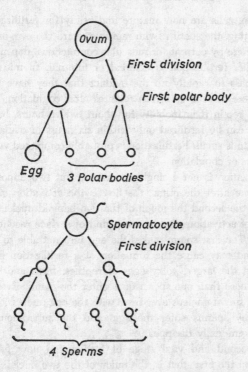

Ovum

First division

First polar body

Egg

3 Polar bodies

Spermatocyte

First division

4 Sperms

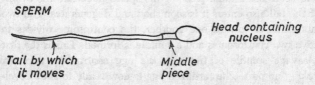

SPERM

Head containing nucleus

Tail by which it moves

Middle piece

[18] *Maturation of sex cells.*

are one ovum and three polar bodies, instead of four ova. This is in contrast to the spermatocyte, which gives rise to four identical sperms. The polar bodies soon degenerate and play no part in the development of the embryo.

The sex cells are now mature and ready for fertilization. After mating, the sperms swim rapidly toward the ova, or are carried there by currents or muscular contractions, depending on whether fertilization is external or internal. In mice the sperms pass so rapidly up the oviduct that they have been found there as soon as fifteen minutes after copulation; they probably retain their mobility for about twelve hours, but as the eggs can be fertilized only within six hours of ovulation, the margin is small. Fertilization is probably completed within two hours of copulation.

Fertilization is not a single occurrence but two important phases one after the other; the first is the activation of the egg and the second the union of the two haploid nuclei. The process of activation may be some kind of surface reaction of the egg. The first sperm makes the egg impenetrable to later sperm and may cause the formation of a fertilization membrane. In the larger, yolky eggs of reptiles, birds and some insects, more than one sperm does enter the ovum. Even so, only one sperm nucleus ever fuses with the egg nucleus, however many sperms enter the egg, and the superfluous remainder gradually disappear.

The second and vital stage of fertilization now follows rapidly on the first—that is, the union of the two nuclei. Only the head and middle piece of the sperm penetrate the ovum; if the tail also enters it is soon shed and degenerates. The two nuclei move toward one another, the centrosome divides to give two centrosomes and a spindle is formed. This is the first cleavage spindle of the egg, the egg centrosome normally taking no part. The fertilized egg is now ready to start development. Although only one sperm fertilizes an egg, or occasionally a small number of sperms penetrate, a vast number of sperms are contained in the emission of most mammals and this seems important for successful fertilization. The average numbers, in millions, of spermatozoa in a single ejaculation of semen for different species of mammals are as follows: Ram

—2500; Bull—4800; Boar—60,000; Man—240. The artificial insemination techniques used in agricultural breeding centers
have shown that a certain minimal quantity of semen is necessary to produce fertilization.

Fertilization in all eggs is followed by a period of rapid
mitotic divisions, the egg dividing into an increasing number
of small cells, the blastomeres. This whole process is called
cleavage. At the beginning of cleavage there is a large un-
divided fertilized egg; at the end of the divisions there is a
ball of small cells called blastomeres, the ball being called a
blastula. While these divisions are going on there is not much
increase in the amount of protoplasm in the blastula; it is
merely divided up into more maneuverable units. Small cells
can move more freely in relation to one another than larger
ones. There is one more advantage of cleavage divisions; the

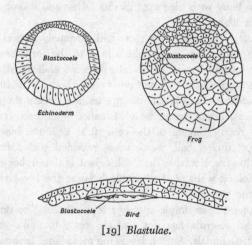

[19] *Blastulae.*

original egg cells are very large in comparison with the size
of normal body cells; at the end of cleavage the blastomeres
have been reduced to something closer to normal body cell
size. These divisions continue until some other process be-

comes more important; they are greatly influenced by the amount of yolk present and the typical end product of cleavage is a hollow ball of cells, the blastula. In very yolky eggs the cleavage may be only partial or even superficial; in partial cleavage the part of the egg that contains the store of yolk does not divide and in superficial cleavage only a small area at one end of the egg divides. In this case, instead of forming a blastula, a small flat plate of cells floats at the upper pole of the egg, forming the blastoderm. This is typical of birds, who have relatively large, yolky eggs.

Eggs really are extraordinary things. It is possible to eat a fertile new-laid hen's egg without there being any indication that it contains all that's necessary to produce a chicken. A human egg can only just be seen with the naked eye and yet it contains the wherewithal not only to develop into a baby, but into a baby with blue eyes like its father and a nose like its grandmother.

Cleavage is followed by a short and extremely critical period. The movements begin which lead to the formation of the basic layers of cells which later become elaborated and specialized into all the different parts of the body. The hollow in the middle of the blastula disappears, and in the simplest case the new arrangement, which is called a gastrula, comes about by rearrangement of the cells; it is as if the blastula were a soft rubber ball, which when prodded with a finger folds in, to give a sizable dent. This dent is the archenteron and the folded walls of the blastula become the two-layered sides of the gastrula.

The process is so simple in only a few animals. The simple two-layered gastrula has not enough scope to make really complicated animals. A third layer, the mesoderm, is essential to vertebrate development. The form and position of the cells that form these three layers in the gastrula are very different from those that they finally take in the embryo.

The transformation of a simple two-layered structure into

a three-layered one is very complicated and cell movement is extensive. Cells roll in from the outer to the inner layers and eventually the embryo, now longer and thinner, starts to develop the rudiments of organ systems. A nervous system, sim-

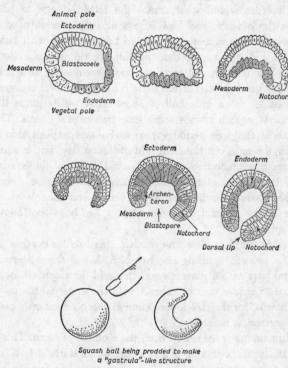

Squash ball being prodded to make a "gastrula"-like structure

[20] *Gastrulation of simple blastula.*

ple gut and muscles, all begin to appear by reorganization of the three basic layers of cells, namely ectoderm, endoderm and mesoderm.

Mammals are quite unique and the early stages of their development are unlike those of any other vertebrates. Except for the monotremes, mammals bear their young alive.

(The monotremes are those animals of Australia that seem to be mammals and yet lay eggs.) During embryonic life food materials are supplied from the maternal blood stream and so the mammalian egg is small, containing very little yolk. No one has discovered what causes the fertilized egg to pass down the oviduct, and how it gets into the uterine tube is uncertain. This mammalian uterine tube is lined with hairs or cilia and it is known that there are rhythmic contractions at ovulation; these two facts are doubtless related, and help the passage of the egg. Since there is little yolk, total cleavage is possible and a little ball of about sixteen cells forms the blastocyst, which spends some time free in the uterus. The length of this free period varies; in humans implantation is usually on or about the sixth post-ovulation day, but in some mammals implantation may be delayed. Some of these cases of delayed implantation have already been described, such as the mouse when it is feeding its young, and animals which mate in the autumn and whose young are born the following spring.

Before implantation the human blastula undergoes a unique process, splitting into two bits. One of these becomes a vital part of the placenta and its rapid development is essential to ensure making contact with the maternal tissues in the uterus, for the developing embryo can get food only after this contact is made.

Human age is measured from the moment of birth. This is not really the beginning of a new life, which starts at fertilization. A pregnancy is reckoned on average to last forty weeks from the start of the last menstrual period. Ovulation actually falls midway between two periods and fertilization takes place soon after. The life of the fertilized egg probably begins, therefore, during the second week of a forty-week pregnancy. During the next thirty-eight weeks this fertilized egg grows and develops to an amazing extent. Although babies are helpless when compared with a young antelope or guinea pig, the changes that take place in those thirty-eight weeks are nonetheless very remarkable. After fertilization the egg travels down the fallopian tube to the uterus and becomes implanted there, about six to eight days after fertilization. When implantation takes place the egg is already divided into a number of cells. Some of these cells will form the embryo and some the extra-embryonic tissues, which, as will be mentioned later, play a very important part in feeding the developing embryo. The embryo is completely surrounded by these tissues which, in their turn, are surrounded by the uterine wall. They thrust minute, fingerlike processes into the wall of the uterus to form the placenta. This is eventually shed as the "afterbirth."

In the early stages the development of the human embryo is very like that of birds and reptiles. All three types of embryo start by laying down the cells that will form the skeleton and nervous system; then a head, heart and tail are discernible and, perhaps rather unexpectedly, there are rudiments of gill pouches. These gill pouches start to disappear by the eighth week, when a human baby has a face with crude features and external ears and is about seven eighths of an inch long, weighing somewhere about a gram. Six weeks later, at fourteen weeks, the face is completely developed, there are external genital organs, and the fetus, as it is now called, is about three inches long and resembles a human child. In these fourteen weeks the fertilized egg has divided repeatedly to become an elaborate structure, but there is still a long way to go before the fetus is capable of independent existence. Movements begin after about eighteen weeks and a doctor can then hear the fetal heartbeats; at this stage the fetus has hair all over, and in some cases this hair persists until the actual birth. During the next fourteen weeks growth is very rapid and by the thirty-second week the baby is generally sufficiently well developed to survive if born, given special care. These babies are called premature, and need to be nursed in special units in a hospital. They have to be kept in incubators and need very specialized feeding; they have developed sufficiently in most ways to be able to live and to grow into perfectly normal adults. A full-term baby, born after forty weeks, has a relatively large head and is still completely helpless. While the young of many animals are able to fend for themselves a few hours after birth, a human baby develops very slowly by comparison. An average baby may be about twenty inches long and seven and a half pounds at birth. It will double this birth weight in the first five months of life. This human child will be dependent on its parents longer than any other young animal, but will finally reach a far greater degree of intelligence and development.

The human fetus grows inside its mother for nine months; this is the gestation period. How is it supplied with food for this long period of development? All mammalian eggs are microscopic, so obviously they cannot contain large quantities of stored food as do the eggs of birds. If the embryo feeds, the foodstuffs must be broken down, and this will make waste products that must be gotten rid of. These two problems are solved by humans and all other mammals by the development of the placenta. Earlier it was mentioned that the human blastula was divided into two parts at a very early stage of its development. These two parts are called the inner cell mass and the trophoblast. It is the trophoblast that helps to form the placenta. There are several different types of placenta, which are formed in a variety of ways, but basically it is made by the fingerlike processes of the trophoblast thrusting into the uterine wall. The structure so formed grows very rapidly at first and by the time the human fetus is born, the baby and placenta weigh much the same amount. At first the placenta surrounds the embryo, but later it becomes localized to one side and connected to it by the umbilical cord, which carries blood vessels to and from the placenta and embryo. These vessels are embryonic and there is no mixing with the mother's blood stream. There are also a large number of maternal blood vessels to the placenta itself; these are separated from the embryonic vessels by very thin walls so that various substances can pass from one blood supply to the other by diffusion. The exchange of dissolved materials between ma-

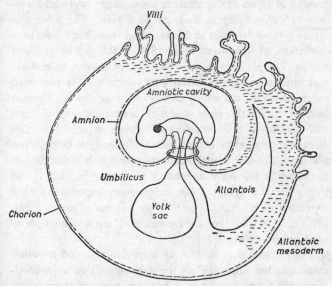

[21] *Embryonic membranes surrounding embryo of placental mammal.*

ternal and embryonic circulations is the essential feature of the placenta. It means foodstuffs can pass from the mother to the embryo and waste products can be gotten rid of in the opposite direction. It also prevents the embryo from becoming permanently attached to the mother, and it has one other vital function which is less obvious. It produces hormones that first help to maintain the pregnancy and later enable the feeding of the baby to continue after birth, by stimulating lactation. The placenta changes in structure as the pregnancy advances, the number of layers separating the maternal and fetal blood supplies getting fewer as time goes on. During the last weeks of pregnancy the fetus shows large increases in weight, probably due to a combination of circumstances. This increase in weight corresponds to the time when the number of layers in the placenta are getting fewer and therefore its permeability is likely to be greater. The fetus also makes greater demands at this time and there is a higher concentration of dissolved foodstuffs in the mother's blood stream. The placenta is, unfortunately, permeable to bacteria and viruses as well as dissolved foodstuffs. It is now well known that children whose mothers have contracted German measles during the early weeks of pregnancy may be born with serious eye or heart defects. The virus responsible for this disease appears to be able to pass to the embryo through the placenta. The fact that the damage occurs only if the disease is caught in the early months of pregnancy has led to the theory that it is in fact the enzyme systems responsible for the formation of heart and eye that are affected. Once the embryonic heart and eyes are formed, they are no longer damaged by the virus.

The placenta is at its most developed in man and the other mammals, but these are not the only animals to have developed this type of structure. There are various others whose young are born alive and who have therefore had to solve the problem of feeding them during their period of gestation, or internal development. The only group of vertebrates whose young are never born alive, as opposed to being laid as an egg, are the birds. The fish, as a group, show a great versatility in the ways in which the embryos are fed. In the elasmobranchs, the group which contains the dogfish, sharks and their relatives, there are several different methods. Some are ovoviviparous. (This term is almost self-explanatory: literally it means "eggs born alive.") The eggs are retained inside the body and so are protected as they develop, but they get their foodstuffs from the yolk they contain. They are brooded in the parent's body rather than in a nest. There is a variation on this method in that the yolk may be absorbed early and the food for the rest of the embryo's development is provided by immature eggs passing from the ovary to the uterus, via the oviducts. Both these methods still depend on yolk granules as the source of food. There is a type of dogfish with a primitive placenta and at least one elasmobranch where the cavity of the yolk sac is filled with cellular strands saturated with circulating blood instead of the usual yolk granules. Here the connection between mother and young in the ripe placenta is entirely vascular, as in mammals. Some bony fish bear their young alive and one, lebistes, appears to feed its embryos by the development of special follicle cells surrounding the eggs which are supplied by an unusually large number of blood vessels.

The amphibians have developed along different lines and, while there are no true cases of viviparity, there are animals where the eggs are kept in the mother's body or where the larval stages appear to have been compressed. The methods used by the amphibia for feeding their developing embryos, where they are born alive rather than laid as eggs, are anything but dull or predictable. No amphibian develops a placenta, but nonetheless some embryos grow inside the mother and are born in a relatively advanced state. There is an African toad whose embryos, although they develop in a mass, each have a vascular tail which emerges from the ball of embryos and makes contact with the wall of the mother's reproductive tract. They are able to obtain nourishment by diffusion, a system not unlike the mammalian placenta. Birds provide food for their young in the eggs but one of the salamanders seems to have elaborated on this idea. They do not provide food for the embryos in the egg, but they do provide a huge number of eggs which form the food for the few embryos which survive and are born. This is interuterine cannibalism. About forty to sixty eggs are fertilized and from one to four young salamanders finally survive to birth. One of the neatest contradictions is shown by the legless amphibians, the apoda. This group have more adaptations to living on land than most of the amphibians and some of them lay large yolky eggs which can develop without water. The contradiction is that the only apoden that bears its young alive is an aquatic one.

Life began in water and the development of animals has been influenced by the steps they have taken to live on land. Amphibia live partly on land; they have learned to breathe air and to move without the support of the surrounding water, but the vast majority have failed to solve the problems of breeding without water. The reptiles became the first large group to manage to breed independently of sea or fresh water, although all groups of land animals have members who return to the water to lay their eggs or bear young. The trouble is that eggs laid on land need support where previously they could just float in the water, and they must be protected against drying up. These problems were overcome by the development of a shell, but this in itself immediately raised a new set of difficulties. If the egg is enclosed in a shell then there must be some means of feeding the embryo and it must also be possible to exchange gases through the shell and remove waste products. Some of the reptiles have solved all these problems along the same lines as the mammals. They develop a type of yolk-sac placenta and do actually produce embryonic membranes, but the placenta remains very simple in structure and there is no invasion of the mother's tissues by the developing embryo, as there is in mammals.

Placentas in mammals vary very widely in their degree of permeability and the number of layers that go into their make-up. In general, the placenta allows substances made up of small molecules, such as sugars and some fats, to pass from mother to embryo, but the proteins, which have large

molecules, and cells cannot pass across. Some animals can
gain from their mother an immunity against various diseases,
but others whose placentas form too formidable a barrier get
a degree of immunization in the very first secretions of the
mammary glands after birth. Before the regular supply of
milk begins to be secreted, the mammary glands provide a
substance called colostrum; it is thicker than milk and different in its chemical composition. As well as providing the
newborn with some degree of immunization, it also contains
a high percentage of nitrogen. It used to be thought of as a
laxative but this theory has now been discounted. Colostrum
probably remains a means of overcoming some of the problems encountered by an embryo in receiving its food entirely
through the placenta.

It has been claimed that being born is the most dramatic
and complete change a human being ever has to undergo.
From the uniform surroundings of the uterus the new individual is thrust into the world to meet a number of completely
new circumstances. The temperature is no longer constant,
there is no support from the surrounding air, which is also
dry. The skeleton must start providing the support needed
and the skin must prevent undue evaporation. The lungs must
expand, which means that the ribs and diaphragm have to
work to pump air in, and the blood from the heart must pass
through the lungs to take up oxygen. Food will be needed
and the kidneys must deal with the excess water and nitrogenous waste produced.

All these changes take place within minutes of the baby's
being born, but what brings about birth? This problem has,
not unexpectedly, been studied more in humans than in any
other animal and the direct causes of birth seem to be complex. The actual mechanical causes are simple enough. The
embryo is expelled by the repeated rhythmical contractions
of the uterus, and followed by the placenta, or "afterbirth."
The conditions that start these rhythmical contractions are

varied. The distention of the uterus is undoubtedly a factor, caused by the accumulation of amniotic fluid. Women who have twins do not usually have a full forty-week pregnancy. This may be due in part to the fact that two babies take up more room than one, and the resultant distention starts off labor. Hormones also play some part in the onset of labor, the concentration of hormones secreted by the placenta probably dropping at the end of the pregnancy. But these processes are not the complete answer. The beginning of labor can be effected by the mother's emotions and probably by stimulation of certain centers of the brain. Emotion, fright and fetal death may cause a woman to go into labor, so the balance is obviously a delicate one controlled by many different factors.

Under normal circumstances the immediate cause of labor is a change in the balance of the hormones present in the mother's blood stream. The hormones secreted by the posterior pituitary gland increase the ability of the uterine muscle to contract rhythmically, but this tendency is inhibited by the hormones secreted by the placenta. By the end of forty weeks the human placenta is beginning to secrete less of these hormones and the change in the balance between the two is sufficient for the contractions of the uterus to start and for the dilation of the cervix to take place, followed by the expulsion of the embryo and the placenta.

The idea of the development of the young inside the mother is a strange one, but the system has advantages. During gestation—that is, the time the embryos develop internally—the mother is vulnerable but the embryos have a safe place, with uniform conditions in which to develop. Their existence is more or less parasitic. The interesting thing is that, in a number of groups of animals, closely related species have solved their reproductive problems quite differently. Some lay eggs, and others, living nearby and in apparently comparable circumstances, bear their young alive. There is a lizard in Texas, called, rather confusingly, a horned "toad." It lives on ants and, when the time comes to breed, digs a hole which may be as much as a foot deep. The leathery-shelled eggs are put in this hole and covered with earth and the mother goes off, leaving no trace of her activities behind her. When the young horned toads hatch, they dig their way to the surface and start to hunt for ants. There would be nothing particularly remarkable in this story if it were not for the fact that in New Mexico there is another species of horned "toad" which behaves very differently. The New Mexican species has no shell glands and the eggs are kept inside the mother's body while they develop. When they are born the young toads emerge in a thin transparent sac, from which they break free, and are immediately ready to fend for themselves. Which species has adopted the better way and why have they such different methods when their way of life is so similar? Is it safer to develop underground or inside the mother? Or is it merely chance that one species developed shell glands and could therefore lay eggs, while the other species either lost, or failed to develop, the glands and therefore had to find another method of protecting its developing young?

This is not an isolated case. Pythons and boas are both large constrictor snakes, many suffocating their prey by strangling them in their coils. The pythons are found from Africa to the Philippines, the boas in Central and South America. They are so alike to the zoologist that they are classified together in the same group, yet pythons lay eggs and boas have their young alive. There is no apparent reason for the difference.

Perhaps the two families of scorpions show a transitional stage. One family, the Buthidae, lay yolky eggs but instead of passing them to the exterior in the ordinary way, they are kept in the mother's body until they hatch and are then born "alive." All their nourishment comes from the egg and the mother only provides a place in which the embryos can develop after the eggs leave the ovary; they are, in fact, ovo-viviparous. The other family of scorpions, Scorpionidae, produce a very different type of egg. It contains no yolk and develops in a side chamber of the mother's egg-laying tract. There is an extension of the egg-laying tube to form a kind of "bottle" and "teat" which is supplied from the mother's gut and to which the embryo becomes attached by well-developed sucking mouth parts. Both types of scorpions are equally well developed when born but the Scorpionidae babies seem a step nearer to true viviparity, though the advantages of such a step are not, at present, apparent.

The placental mammals appear to have solved the problem of retaining their young in their bodies and the development of the placenta ensures food for the embryo and a mechanism whereby it can obtain gases for respiration and get rid of waste products. But the mammals themselves show a gradation from egg laying to this state of highly organized internal development. The peculiar mammals of the Australian continent, the duck-billed platypus and the spiny ant-eater of the monotremes, still lay eggs which they incubate, but also have a type of mammary gland from which they feed their young after hatching.

The next group of mammals, the marsupials or pouched mammals such as kangaroos and wallabies, form the link between the egg-laying monotremes and the placental mammals. These pouched mammals bear their young alive but in a very immature state. Like the monotremes they are mostly found in Australasia, except for the opossums, which live on the American continent. The eggs of the marsupials are minute and resemble those of the placental mammals rather than the large yolky eggs of the monotremes; they are fertilized in the normal way but the gestation period is very short —in some cases as little as ten days and never more than six weeks. The newborn marsupial has a very well-developed mouth and forelimbs, but is naked, blind and deaf, with only rudimentary hind legs. It crawls by means of its forelimbs from the mother's genital opening to the pouch, or folds of skin, that surround the milk glands. There it attaches itself to a teat and, until it is old enough to suck, the milk is pumped down its throat by the mother. It remains in the pouch for another two months and when it finally emerges is a miniature replica of its parents. This seems a halfway stage in development between the egg-laying monotremes and the placental mammals, where the young have a long period of development in the mother and are born in a relatively advanced state.

The development of mammals is such a delicate process that it is possible for things to go wrong at almost any stage. If the time interval between ovulation and mating is too long there may be irregularities in the mechanism of fertilization; or these may be caused by abnormalities in the seminal fluid or ovum membranes. These mishaps are hard to trace, as the embryos are either reabsorbed or expelled.

Even if fertilization is successful the embryo is still exposed to a variety of hazards. Some of the most tragic congenital malformations in children are due to the mother's contracting syphilis. Both viruses and bacteria seem to be able to pass from mother to child through the placenta; German measles has already been mentioned as causing eye and heart defects in the developing child. Contagious abortion in cattle is due to a similar type of infection, only here the embryo dies.

Nesting sites chosen by birds and reptiles are often unsuitable, and the eggs are lost. Mammals do not escape this sort of situation, for they cannot always provide the conditions necessary for a successful pregnancy. If the mother is too old, severely undernourished or in poor health, she will be unable to support the developing embryo. The blood groups of mother and embryo may be incompatible, the mother may get toxemia, suffer from low hormone concentration, have a defective uterus or an infection of the reproductive tract. This catalogue of disasters could go on and on. Any one of these things will lead either to prenatal death or a malformed child. It is therefore truly remarkable that millions of normal, healthy children are born each year, having avoided so many pitfalls during their forty weeks' development.

So many different patterns of development appear in the animal world. Some animals lay eggs; some keep the eggs inside their own bodies, offering food and protection during development. Many others have added a stage to their life history: the eggs hatch as larvae, which grow for a time before turning into the adult form. These larval stages fulfill a variety of functions, but two that come immediately to mind are the larval stages of sessile animals. These animals, such as the barnacle, remain attached to one spot or a very limited locality all their lives, but by having a free-living larva are able to spread over a far wider area and avoid overcrowding. In other animals, notably insects, the larval stage allows for a period of feeding and growth and the adult is then concerned solely with reproduction. The cabbage white butterfly does no damage itself but its larva, the caterpillar, will decimate a field of cabbages. The feeding and growth is done by the voracious caterpillar; this then pupates and the adult butterfly that emerges from the pupa concentrates on finding a mate and starting another generation.

It seems there is no answer to the question of which is the best way for a new generation to enter the world. Twenty-eight million ling eggs floating in the ocean, four robin's eggs incubated by the mother, one human baby born after forty weeks in the uterus. As long as sufficient survive to maturity, replenishing the numbers of the species, it seems that the end justifies the means, and there are a host of different ways of solving the same problem.

14

What Next?

If you believe in evolution, in the survival of the fittest in a competitive world, you will wonder how man is evolving now. The parents least able to support them are having the most children. The sick are being kept alive. The number of births per family bears no relation to the intelligence, strength or well-being of the parents. Yet evolution, according to most evolutionists, must be acting somehow, and urging the human population along in some direction, even if it is to a level of greater stupidity. Just what is going to happen next? Thirty million people die a year who need not have died had elementary medical care been given to them. Yet, despite this number, the world's population will have doubled by the end of this century. The problems are immense and are becoming larger.

Yet the last hundred years have seen enormous progress in all fields of zoology. It is only during this time that man has had any comprehension of such things as why children look like their parents, or indeed how animals and plants are able to reproduce at all. Now it is essential that the knowledge gained is used for the general benefit of mankind.

One of the most pressing problems is equating the world's food supply with its ever increasing population. There is a huge discrepancy between the output of Europe and Asia, between North and South America; the Food and Agriculture Organization calculates that advanced countries produce ten times more food per head than the backward lands. Yet the underdeveloped countries account for nearly three quarters of the total population in the world. Even in a country such as Britain there is no room for complacency. Farms run on proper scientific lines are able to produce twice the national average, while the average British cow has a yield four times that of one from a backward area of Europe.

Artificial insemination centers are being set up throughout Britain. This means that even the smallest farmer has the opportunity to breed from pedigree bulls. If proper breeding schemes were implemented, the yields of many herds could be doubled in two generations. It is hard enough to get such progress in this country, where the level of education is comparatively high. It is far more vital that these methods be introduced in Africa and the East, where agricultural improvements must go hand in hand with general education.

One of the advantages of artificial insemination is that it allows a first-class bull to mate with ten times as many cows as would be possible if he just ran with a herd. So far it has not been possible to exploit the advantages of a pedigree female animal in the same way, but a start has been made. The embryos can be removed from one strain of sheep at an early stage in their development, flown across the world and grafted into an inferior animal. This means that a cross-bred female of uncertain pedigree can have pedigree young. The necessary techniques are still in the early stages and the process is not yet economical on a large scale. Even now it is more convenient to fly half a dozen embryos round the world than the same number of adult or young animals. If this idea can be developed it should provide another way of upgrading the standard of breeding animals in the backward areas of Africa and Asia more rapidly than would be possible by natural means.

The research on the breeding of animals has produced a lot of valuable information, on the structure of spermatozoa and the properties of semen as well as on more general topics of animal genetics. This work has gone on in conjunction with similar work on plants. It is useless to produce improved strains of cattle and sheep if there is nothing on which they can feed. Experimental work has produced types of grasses and cereals that not only have a higher yield but are also more resistant to bad weather conditions and disease. Nearly 90% of the maize sown in the cornbelt of Canada and the U.S.A. is a new variety. This strain was produced by crossing two specially selected inbred lines. The resultant hybrid is so much better that in places the yield has increased by as much as 25%. Botanists have managed to produce a kind of wheat that is not only very productive but also resistant to rust fungus. This fungus is one of the worst pests of the wheat-fields of North America. This sort of work is of inestimable value and now it may be possible to improve the varieties of rice in the same sort of way.

It is essential that all land should become more productive. What about the sea? The wastage in the fish population is very large; if fish could be husbanded in some way, there would be a valuable additional source of food. Scientists have already tried to increase the growth of edible fish by adding chemicals to the sea, in much the same way as a farmer uses artificial fertilizers. These chemicals encourage the growth of the minute plants which are the basis of all sea life. These microscopic plants provide the food for the smallest animals which in their turn feed the larger sea creatures and their role is somewhat similar to grass on land. It is also possible to influence the nature of the foodstuffs synthesized by these plants. Further work along these lines may make the sea a great deal more productive, and if the plants are made to have a high fat content, they could form valuable animal-feeding stuffs, or even human food.

The study of genetics has led to great improvements in the breeding stock of both animals and plants, helping both farmer and gardener. The minute plants in the sea have begun to be studied. The improvement of microscopes has opened many new fields in the study of minute living things. Now bacteria and viruses are getting a great deal of attention, not only in the study of disease, but in finding uses to which they can profitably be put. Bacteria are already employed in sewage disposal, and yeasts have been used for thousands of years to make bread and alcoholic drinks. Now it seems likely that some molds and bacteria may be bred that will be able to make complex organic compounds which at present can be synthesized only by purely chemical means.

Geneticists have made many of these advances possible by supplying valuable information about the ways characters are passed from one generation to the next, but their contribution also covers other fields. They have found out a great deal about the genes which actually control inherited characteristics and about the structure of the chromosomes which carry these genes. In a sexually reproducing animal the chromosomes are contributed to the fertilized egg by each parent in approximately equal numbers. Numerous experiments on the fruit fly Drosophila have shown that it is possible to determine the order in which the genes lie along the chromosome. While the exact structure of these genes is unknown, they are apparently affected by contact with X rays, alpha particles, high-speed electrons and other forms of ionizing radiation. These radiations cause genetic changes which are then inherited in the normal way. These changes are called mutations and are generally harmful, which is hardly surprising in view of the sensitivity of the mechanism involved. Occasionally a change is advantageous, and such changes, arising naturally, are probably responsible for general evolutionary progress. At present breeding experiments rely on the random occurrence of new combinations of existing genes. But with the development of electronics it may soon be possible to choose which mutation is produced. The harmful mutations would be rejected, only those which improve the breed being kept. Such experiments should not be too difficult when using plants and simple animals, and as the techniques for transplanting placental embryos improve it should become possible with higher animals. How far such methods are practicable depends on the degree of accuracy with which the electronic beam can be directed on a particular area of a chromosome. Should it be feasible, it will mean that the range of variation, and the speed of breeding new stocks, will be enormously increased.

A geneticist can also help in human problems. Many diseases and abnormalities are now known to have a hereditary basis. This knowledge has led a number of couples to question whether or not they should marry relations or, if married, whether they can have children. So few of these abnormalities are known to be due to a single gene that the answer is rarely a simple one. Usually the best that can be done is to advise the parents of the risks involved and the mathematical probability of their child's having a certain abnormality. Also with improved methods of chromosome counting it is now beginning to be possible to help in other ways. Mongoloid children have been found to have one autosome in triplicate, rather than in duplicate as in a normal cell. Work is going on to see whether the parents of such children have anything abnormal in their own chromosome counts, to find out if such abnormality is likely to be repeated in subsequent pregnancies.

The greatest of all human problems in which the geneticist can help, however, is that of population control. It is extremely hard to predict population changes, and most of the forecasts made in the last hundred years have been very inaccurate, although based on well-informed data. In civilized countries the controlling factors have ceased to be biological; with good medical services and a high standard of living the population is not limited by the available food or disease, but by the wishes of the people. It has been shown that modern governments can do quite a lot to influence population trends. In France the population was steady for a number of years, but the introduction of family allowances led to a rise in the birth rate. It is not hard to provide economic incentives to have children in these days of heavy taxation.

There seems to be no basic human instinct for a family; in primitive societies children are the inevitable result of the sex impulse, and in civilized communities the desire for children is rationalized and influenced by public and religious opinions and economic motives. The real problem lies in the underdeveloped countries of the world. If the rate at which the population was increasing a few years ago persists, the entire population of India will be duplicated in eight years. The general rise in populations the world over is 3% per annum. When one considers that this is mainly confined to India, China, Central and South America and Africa, all countries with poorly developed agricultural methods, the problem of feeding and maintaining the increasing millions is indeed a serious one. Some of the answer lies in improving food production as already mentioned, but this will be useless unless some methods are devised for limiting the populations of these rapidly expanding countries.

There is a great need for some reliable means of fertility control. Even if this is found there are still many problems to be overcome. Many religions of the world preach against limiting birth and are for the conservation of life; some of these religions have modified this teaching of recent years but are still against the more drastic methods of fertility control. In man it is necessary to separate the sex desire and the reproductive process. This has happened to a certain extent in Europe and America, and there has been a sharp drop in the birth rate since the introduction of contraception. A survey of a group of couples in the United States showed that 74% had the number of children they wanted and most of the remainder had only one child more than the chosen number. This was due to contraception and family planning, yet even in the United States there are problems. There is a great loss of farm land to roads and buildings, there is a limit both to the amount of water available and the amount of non-renewable minerals. In other parts of the world some form of fertility control is essential if spreading poverty and social degradation are to be avoided. No animal species has ever been known to reproduce without limit; there is either a high mortality or a low fertility rate. Man has the choice.

What are the prospects for fertility control? In ancient times and, more recently, among primitive populations, the population was prevented from increasing too rapidly by the practice of infanticide. The killing of children was limited by strict laws and taboos that prevented undue fluctuations in numbers. These customs are now more or less extinct and should remain so. Other primitive methods of limiting populations included the castration, or complete unsexing, of members of the community under the guise of religious ceremonies, and again these practices have been more or less abandoned.

A less drastic method of limiting reproduction that has been used for centuries lies in the use of plant materials. Herbal and other plant concoctions have been dispensed through the ages with apparent success, although the reason for their efficacy has not been understood. It is now known that some plants contain chemical substances, such as steroids and hormonal agents, that have no effect on the plant itself but may affect any animal that eats it. In some of the more barren parts of Australia a new type of clover was introduced that enabled desert land to be used for grazing sheep. All went well until it was found that the sheep were sterile. Investigation showed that the new strain of clover contained the hormone estrogen, which inhibited reproduction. There is a need for a great deal of research to be done on these plants, since they may provide a safe and practical way of controlling reproduction.

One of the chief disadvantages of the methods of birth control practiced in Europe and America is that they are quite unsuitable to the areas of the world which need them most. Present-day methods are either too expensive for the millions of India or Puerto Rico or require too much of backward people. What methods of fertility control are likely to prove of any value?

Some scientists have advocated that governments institute sterilization bonuses. This scheme has the advantage that it would appeal to the groups of lowest intelligence and with the lowest standard of living and help to raise the general standard of the population. Sterilization is now possible by minor surgery. Either the vas deferens in the male or the fallopian tubes in the female can be tied or ligatured, leaving the general sexual impulses and behavior of the individual unimpaired. In Japan, which has already started to deal with this problem of a rising population, women are sterilized by cauterization. This involves touching the point where the fallopian tubes join the uterus with a red-hot rod and when the tissues heal the fallopian tubes are sealed. This operation has the advantage that it can be performed in the outpatient section of a hospital and in Japan, if unsuccessful and followed by pregnancy, the woman may have a legal abortion and a further cauterization. Medical authorities claim a high percentage of success with no ill effects to the patient. To be effective this method needs a program of education and propaganda and in many countries would still be unacceptable on religious grounds.

Some doctors have tried placing a gold or silver spiral in the uterus where the normal movements of the uterine muscles cause the ring to move and so prevent implantation, should fertilization occur. The experimental results are not yet sufficient to show whether this method has any widespread use and it is probable that the amount of medical attention necessary would make it unsuitable for underdeveloped countries.

Lately there has been a certain amount of publicity for oral methods of contraception. Hormonal agents are known which affect nearly every stage of the female's estrus cycle and they can be eaten. The pills developed recently and tried out both in Puerto Rico and on volunteers in Britain seem to avoid some of the undesirable side effects previously associated with these substances. One of the chief disadvantages seems to be that they must be taken regularly for twenty-one days out of every twenty-eight and if given up may leave the patient with increased, rather than diminished, fertility.

Many people advocate the rhythm method of birth control. This involves neither drugs nor appliances and is approved by religious bodies that frown on other methods. It is based on the theory that the life of the ovum lasts only twenty-four hours after ovulation, and that of a sperm only forty-eight hours after emission. If there is no intercourse at the time of ovulation then fertilization is impossible. Beads have been devised for primitive peoples that enable them to count out the days between one menstrual period and the next to avoid having intercourse on those days when fertilization can occur. There is no agreement in medical circles on the efficacy of this method, however, and women certainly show great variations in the number of days between successive ovulations, so that it is difficult to predict the fertile period with any great degree of accuracy.

A line of investigation still in its early stages deals with the possibility of postponing conception by a method similar to immunization against a disease. Immunity from a disease is gained by injecting the patient with antigens which cause substances called antibodies to form in the blood. These antibodies will attack a specific disease if it invades the body—

for example, smallpox. Each type of organism contains specific proteins against which it is possible to develop antibodies. Sperm, ova and embryonic tissues contain specific protein too, against which it is possible to develop antibodies in just the same way. The experiments carried out so far have failed to yield a reliable method for producing infertility, but it may be possible to suspend fertility for a period of six to twelve months and perhaps to extend this period by further booster injections.

One of the chief requirements of any method of birth control is that it should be cheap, and the second necessity is that it should be as foolproof as possible. A line of investigation that has proved promising deals with the possibility of introducing bacteria into the female reproductive tract. There are various associations between animals and plants in nature where they live together to their mutual benefit; this is called symbiosis. There are simple plants in the human intestine which help in digestion and gain their nourishment from their human host. Some women who are apparently sterile have been found to have bacteria in their vagina and uterus; when these bacteria are removed by antibiotics, conception takes place. It is now hoped that a form of bacteria may be found which can be seeded in the genital tract and will act as a protection against fertilization until removed by antibiotics. So far seeding has been carried out successfully, but the strains used live for a very short time. Before the method can be used on a large scale, either a longer-seeding variety of bacteria must be found or some means of introducing the shorter-seeding forms once or twice a month must be developed in capsule form, for example.

The problems of the future are many, but they are not necessarily insoluble. The rising populations of some countries of the world must be checked, and it is a problem of which the whole world should be made aware. There seems little point in feeding the hungry of these deprived nations now, if the people are merely being kept alive in order that five times as many may die some years hence. Some form of fertility control must go hand in hand with the schemes to increase the world's food supply.

One of the causes of tension at present concerns the controversies that surround the vexing question of race relations. Few people can view these issues dispassionately; they either feel ashamed that anyone should assume the color of a man's skin makes him different, or they are appalled at the prospect of mixed marriages and complete racial equality. There is no scientific evidence one way or the other to show whether complete racial intermixing would be a good or a bad thing. In the field of athletics there is little to choose between the potential abilities of any race; those who gain Olympic fame seem to depend as much on training and environment as heredity. But man's mental capacity is the thing that has changed most rapidly since he started to evolve and there may be significant differences between the mental capacities of different races. It seems that some completely unbiased research into the effects of mixed marriages is necessary, otherwise peoples of different races will either be subjected to unnecessary restrictions or encouraged to mix to such an extent that the whole human race will suffer.

Another problem is going to be to ensure that the intelligent members of the community continue to have children at nearly the same rate as the stupid. The present-day system of education and taxation in England is such that the people who are best fitted to provide the next generation cannot afford to do so and still maintain their social and economic level. By educating the intelligent children of poorer families and enabling them to do more skilled jobs, the state is also reducing the likelihood of their having large families, since they have a new place in society to maintain and no capital behind them. Some system is needed to encourage the both intelligent and fit to have families and discourage those of lower intelligence. One of the political problems of the future, with increased mechanization and automation, is going to be keeping the stupid fully employed.

Perhaps one of the chief dangers lies in the establishment of a truly scientific dictatorship. Such a state was described by Aldous Huxley in his book *Brave New World*. At the time this book was written the state envisaged by the author was in the realms of science fiction, but recent advances have made it more possible. There is a danger of overorganization as well as overpopulation. It seems possible scientifically that, in the not too distant future, the breeding of humans could be as highly controlled as that of a herd of cattle. It is already possible to store seminal fluid almost indefinitely by freezing, and methods are also being developed for preserving ova. When these are perfected it is only a small step to artificial fertilization and implantation. Men and women could then store germ cells, accept surgical sterilization and use artificial methods to develop a family as desired. This is closely akin to the process Huxley described, where grades of humans were produced by state control, while drugs and indoctrination kept them in a contented frame of mind. Such a world, without individualism and discontent, is also without hope.

The hope for the future lies in the fact that the human brain has already evolved a long way from that of the apes, and even further from that of the jellyfish. There is no reason to suppose that it has reached the limits of this development. If the population of the world can be kept within bounds while this development goes on, there appear to be new worlds to conquer and great possibilities for the species as a whole. Francis Bacon summed things up when he wrote nearly four hundred years ago:

> Man must pursue things which are just in present,
> and leave the future to the divine Providence.

Index